A PROPHET CALLED ISAIAH

THE CALLED
BOOK 2

KENNETH A. WINTER

WildernessLessons

JOIN MY READERS' GROUP FOR UPDATES AND FUTURE RELEASES

Please join my Readers' Group so i can send you a free book, as well as updates and information about future releases, etc.

See the back of the book for details on how to sign up.

A Prophet Called Isaiah

"The Called" - Book 2 (a series of novellas)

Published by:

Kenneth A. Winter

WildernessLessons, LLC

Richmond, Virginia

United States of America

kenwinter.org

wildernesslessons.com

Edited by Sheryl Martin Hash

Cover design by Scott Campbell Design

ISBN 978-1-7367155-6-7 (soft cover)

ISBN 978-1-7367155-7-4 (e-book)

ISBN 978-1-7367155-8-1 (large print)

Library of Congress Control Number: 2021925004

DEDICATION

Now these are the gifts Christ gave to the church: the apostles, the prophets, the evangelists, and the pastors and teachers.
Ephesians 4:11

∾

In memory of Keith Thomas,
and in honor of the many others whom God has also used over the years to speak truth into my life.

∾

CONTENTS

FROM THE AUTHOR

A word of explanation for those of you who are new to my writing.

You will notice that whenever i use the pronoun "I" referring to myself, i have chosen to use a lowercase "i." This only applies to me personally (in the Preface). i do not impose my personal conviction on any of the characters in this book. It is not a typographical error. i know this is contrary to proper English grammar and accepted editorial style guides. i drive editors (and "spell check") crazy by doing this. But years ago, the Lord convicted me – personally – that in all things i must decrease and He must increase.

And as a way of continuing personal reminder, from that day forward, i have chosen to use a lowercase "i" whenever referring to myself. Because of the same conviction, i use a capital letter for any pronoun referring to God throughout the entire book. The style guide for the New Living Translation (NLT) does not share that conviction. However, you will see that i have intentionally made that slight revision and capitalized any pronoun referring to God in my quotations of Scripture from the NLT. If i have violated any style guides as a result, please accept my apology, but i must honor this conviction.

Lastly, regarding this matter – this is a <u>personal</u> conviction – and i share it only so you will understand why i have chosen to deviate from normal editorial practice. i am in no way suggesting or endeavoring to have anyone else subscribe to my conviction. Thanks for your understanding.

～

PREFACE

~

This fictional novella is part of a series titled, *The Called*, which is about ordinary people God called to use in extraordinary ways. We often tend to elevate the people we read about in Scripture and place them on a pedestal far beyond our reach. We think, "Of course God used them. They had extraordinary strength or extraordinary faith. But God could never use an ordinary person like me."

That is a lie the evil one would love for us to believe. He would love for us to think we can't possibly be used by God because we are too ordinary. But the reality is that throughout history God has used the ordinary to accomplish the extraordinary – and He has empowered them through His Holy Spirit.

This story is about the life of one of those ordinary people – Isaiah, the prophet. Like many of you, throughout much of my life, i have been greatly encouraged by the promises contained in the book of Isaiah. Most notably, the Lord chose Isaiah to announce many of the promises related to the coming Messiah. We remember many of those prophecies each year at Christmastime as we recall how they were fulfilled through the advent of Jesus.

But the promises do not stop with the first coming of Jesus. The promises continue to point to the realities that will be fulfilled in the second coming of Jesus – when He returns to establish His kingdom on earth from the throne He will establish in the new Jerusalem. All things will be made new, and as George Frideric Handel wrote using some of Isaiah's words in his great work, "Messiah, an Oratorio," our returning Lord will reign forever and ever. Oh, what a day that will be!

My familiarity with those promises from the book Isaiah was my motivation for writing this story about the person of Isaiah. The foundation for this novella comes from the books of 2 Kings, chapters 12 through 21; 2 Chronicles, chapters 24 through 33, as well as Isaiah itself. As I began to study those passages more closely, i became increasingly aware of the family relationship Isaiah had with the kings of Judah, specifically kings Uzziah, Jotham, Ahaz, Hezekiah, and Manasseh. These were the kings to whom God was directing Isaiah to deliver what, in many instances, were very difficult messages.

The family relationships bring to light an internal conflict Isaiah may have felt when God compelled him to convey those messages. Also, because Isaiah had been close to the kings growing up, he had a unique platform from which to write about the One who will one day sit on the throne of Judah – the One who is King of kings and Lord of lords. But don't lose sight of the fact that Isaiah was a flawed, ordinary man placed in God-ordered circumstances to be a follower through whom God would accomplish extraordinary things.

So, i hope you will sit back and enjoy this walk through Isaiah's life. The story, though based on the Scriptures i have already mentioned, has also been shaped by the writings of Josephus, the early historian of the church, and by certain rabbinical teachings recorded in the Talmud. On a number of occasions, i have added fictional elements to help fill in missing details about Isaiah's story. My goal is not to detract from Scripture in any way; rather, I want to help Isaiah's personal story become even more alive in our minds and in our hearts as we read his writings.

Most of the characters in the story come directly from Scripture – you will easily recognize them. However, where the Bible is silent, i have chosen to add background details about the characters that are either fictional or conjectures not confirmed in Scripture. These details are added to further the telling of the story. As i already mentioned, a few of the characters are completely fictional.

Throughout the stories, some instances of dialogue are direct quotes from Scripture. Whenever i am quoting Scripture, you will find that it has been italicized. The Scripture references are included in the back of this book. Those remaining instances of dialogue not italicized are part of the fictional story in order to help advance the storyline. However, i have endeavored to use Scripture as the basis in forming any added dialogue spoken by a historical character with the intent that i do not detract from the overall message of God's Word.

Finally, my prayer is, that as you read this story, you will see Isaiah, his family, and the kings of Judah through new eyes – and be challenged to hear and see the prophecies of God through their eyes. And most importantly, you will be challenged to be an "ordinary" follower with the willingness and faith to be used by God in extraordinary ways … for His glory!

∼

1

A PROPHET'S EXAMPLE

~

 y grandfather, King Joash, was the eighth king of our southern kingdom of Judah. Approximately 100 years before his reign, the nation of Israel split into two kingdoms – the northern kingdom, which retained the name Israel, and the southern kingdom taking the name Judah, the tribal name of King David.

I was sitting in the Great Hall of the palace several years ago, dressed in my royal splendor, thinking how privileged I was to be a member of the royal line of David, Solomon, and Joash. Jotham, the coregent (joint ruler) at the time, was addressing routine matters brought before him. I watched him, thinking surely there were other officials in the palace who could preside over such trivial matters.

Suddenly, a servant announced the arrival of a prophet of God named Amos, who said he needed to speak with the coregent at once. I had heard of Amos; he was born here in Judah but moved to Israel after he declared God was sending him there.

· · ·

Amos was originally a shepherd from the rural area of Tekoa here in Judah. He had no special training as a prophet, but apparently Jehovah God called him to leave the grazing fields to carry His message to the palace of Israel. It sounded a little questionable to me.

He did not wait for Jotham to direct him forward. Rather, he boldly approached the throne and began speaking, with no regard for the official he had just interrupted.

"Coregent," Amos began, "you must listen to this message from the Lord that Jeroboam II, king of Israel, has rejected. This is what the Lord says: '*O people of Israel and Judah – the entire family I rescued from Egypt – from among all the families on the earth, I chose you alone.*[1]

"'*That is why I must punish you for all your sins. When the war trumpet blares, shouldn't the people be alarmed? When disaster comes to a city, isn't it because the Lord planned it? But always, first of all, I warn you through my servants the prophets. I, the Sovereign Lord, have now done this.*[2]

"'*The lion has roared – tremble in fear! The Sovereign Lord has spoken – I dare not refuse to proclaim His message!*'[3]

"And coregent, *this is what the Lord says* specifically *to the people of Judah: 'You have sinned again and again, and I will not forget it. I will not let you go unpunished any longer! You have rejected the laws of the Lord, refusing to obey Me. You have been led astray by the same lies that deceived your ancestors. So I will send fire down upon you, and all the fortresses of Jerusalem will be destroyed.*'"[4]

I watched closely for Jotham's reaction. Would he become angry as the king of Israel had done? Would he have the prophet forcibly removed? What would he say? I didn't need to wait long for his answer.

. . .

"May God be merciful to His servant, Jotham, and to the people He has set apart for Himself! Forgive us of our sins, O God, and turn Your wrath away from us.

"Amos, what can I do to appease God's wrath and lead our people to do what is right in His eyes?"

Jotham's humble and contrite response surprised me. He obviously viewed this prophet as someone who was highly credible. I realized then how great a burden the weight of this counsel was for this prophet of God.

I had witnessed many bring their counsel before the king over the years, including me. But I had rarely seen that counsel borne from such godly wisdom.

As Jotham listened intently to Amos's every word, I knew his desire was to lead the people back to a right relationship with God. I realized that despite our lifelong friendship, I would never have the influence over Jotham that this prophet of God did.

At that moment, I came face to face with a sense of my own inadequacy and my own insignificance. I began to envy this prophet of God. Though he smelled like sheep and dressed in tatters, I realized he was the most important person in the room – even more important than the coregent himself. He was delivering a message from Jehovah God, and there was nothing of greater consequence than that!

∼

2

MY EARLY YEARS IN THE PALACE

∼

My father, Amoz, and his much older brother, Amaziah, were the sons of King Joash. My grandfather was assassinated by two of his trusted advisers while my father was still a young lad, so I know him only through the stories I'm told. My uncle Amaziah became the ninth king of Judah.

I never knew my uncle either because he was assassinated twenty-five years before I was born. He had provoked a war with the northern kingdom of Israel. During that war, his army suffered a humiliating defeat that led to portions of Jerusalem being destroyed and the treasury of the temple and the kingdom being pillaged. The people of Judah blamed my uncle for the defeat, and it was several of his officers who murdered him.

His son, Uzziah, became the tenth king of Judah when he was only sixteen years old. He, however, quickly gained favor with the people. The nation prospered under his leadership and again achieved the wealth and prestige it had enjoyed during the reign of my ancestor King Solomon.

· · ·

Cousin Uzziah refortified the walls of Jerusalem and strengthened its defenses by placing machines on the wall towers at the gates that would shoot arrows and hurl large stones. He reorganized and reequipped the army into an effective fighting force. He successfully introduced new methods of agriculture and had a multitude of water cisterns dug throughout the land.

Why was King Uzziah so successful? Two reasons. First, he did what was pleasing in God's sight and enjoyed His favor. Second, he did what was pleasing because he sought God and heeded the wise counsel of the prophet Zechariah.

By the time I was born, Uzziah had already reigned for twenty-five years and was widely respected abroad, even to the entrance of Egypt. Growing up as a member of the royal family in his palace, I, too, enjoyed the many privileges a favored king possesses – though I was far removed from the order of royal succession.

Jotham, Uzziah's eldest son – my first cousin once removed – was, in fact, the heir to the throne. He was two years younger than I, so we became fast friends early on. People used to tell us we were inseparable, much like our fathers had been during their childhood.

When I was seven and Jotham was five, his mother gave birth to a little girl, Nebiah. By the time she was old enough to walk, she began to join Jotham and me on our adventures instead of playing at home with her sisters. We tried everything we could to discourage Nebiah, but nothing worked, and soon the three of us were almost constant companions. To tell the truth, as I got older, I actually started to enjoy her company.

Prince Jotham and I shared the same tutors and received the same quality of education. Eventually we became very competitive in just about everything, including our academic studies, our hunting skills, and our athletic pursuits. We often slipped away from the palace and spent our afternoons exploring the hills outside of Jerusalem. I'm not sure which we enjoyed more – escaping the watchful eyes of our chaperones or exploring the countryside.

·· • •

Jotham, Nebiah, and I were exploring some caves outside the city one day when a messenger arrived with a rather stern note for Jotham. We were to return to the palace immediately! We knew we must be in trouble but couldn't figure out why this adventure was causing more of a stir than our previous ones.

When we got to the palace, Jotham was directed into the Great Hall to see his father while Nebiah and I were told to wait outside. He came out a little while later, looking very somber.

"My father has done something terrible!" Jotham exclaimed. "Apparently, he entered the Lord's sanctuary in the temple this morning and personally burned incense on the altar."

We all knew that was something only priests whom God has set apart for that work should do. Not even the king has been given that privilege by God.

"The high priest, Azariah, together with eighty other priests entered the sanctuary and confronted my father saying, *'It is not for you to burn incense to the Lord. Get out of the sanctuary for you have sinned. The Lord God will not honor you for this!'*[1]

"Father was furious they had spoken to him in such a way, and he refused to set down the incense burner he was holding. But suddenly the ground underneath the temple began to shake!"

~

3

THE COREGENCY OF UZZIAH AND JOTHAM

~

"The shaking of the ground under the temple was so violent the walls and ceiling of the temple began to shift," Jotham continued. "Within moments, a fissure appeared in the exterior masonry wall, and the sun shone brightly across my father's face. The priests turned ashen as they looked in horror at my father.

"His forehead was suddenly covered with leprosy, and it quickly began to spread! The priests rushed him out of the temple, and he secluded himself in the Great Hall. He is planning to move into a nearby house isolated from everyone else. He has designated me to be his coregent over the palace and the government!"

At the age of twenty, Jotham's life had radically changed ... and so had mine. He was no longer the carefree, fun-loving, self-indulgent son of a king; he was now my ruler. We had always known this day would come, but we hadn't expected it to occur so soon!

Up until that moment, my role had always been as Jotham's companion and friend. I was there to encourage him and, on occasion, give him a word of counsel. But now, there were many royal advisers who would step into that role.

Jotham invited me to sit in the Great Hall once he assumed his position on the throne. I had no official role other than that of being his trusted friend. But I did listen with interest as the affairs of the nation were discussed and decided.

One of the outcomes of King Uzziah's reign was the strengthening of what he saw as two critical alliances. One alliance was to strengthen the kingdom from within, and the other was an alliance he made outside the kingdom.

Soon after Jotham was made coregent, his father arranged for him to marry Princess Ahio. She was the daughter of Azrikam, an influential and wealthy leader of the tribe of Benjamin. He was a descendant of our first king, Saul, also of the tribe of Benjamin.

The marriage was arranged to strengthen the unity of the two tribes that together form the southern kingdom of Judah. It was a uniting of the house of Saul with the house of David. Though it had been over 150 years since the other ten tribes of the nation of Israel had divided to form the kingdom of Israel to the north, Uzziah wanted to assure the alliance of the two remaining tribes remained strong.

The alliance he formed outside the kingdom was with the Assyrians. Uzziah knew all too well that his father's downfall was a result of his defeat by the northern kingdom. Though Judah had not been destroyed, the defeat was unmistakable. Uzziah knew if Israel had been allied with the Assyrians, Judah would have been annihilated.

He fully intended that no such union would ever come to pass. The best way to ensure that was for him to establish a strong coalition with the Assyrians. He received his greatest assistance in establishing that alliance from the northern kingdom of Israel itself. They had subsequently chosen to join forces with the king of the Arameans – the enemy of the Assyrians.

The adage, "the enemy of my enemy is my friend" certainly rang true, and King Uzziah and King Tiglath-Pileser III of Assyria entered a mutually advantageous partnership.

Less than a year after their marriage, Ahio and Jotham had a son, Ahaz, the heir to the throne. With Jotham now completely absorbed in his responsibilities as coregent, husband, and father, he and I spent little time together. I soon found myself passing more and more time with Nebiah.

Over time, Nebiah's and my friendship developed into something more. The entire palace started to notice our relationship, including her mother, Queen Jerushah. One day, I received a summons to come before Jotham.

"Isaiah," he said, "I would not normally be the one to have this conversation with you. But as you know, my father is unable to allow anyone to see him, so the responsibility has fallen to me. He and my mother have both been in communication with me regarding the growing interest between you and my sister, Nebiah.

"My father has always seen marriage as a way to form political alliances – as demonstrated by my own marriage. He intends to have my sister marry someone who will further strengthen our political agreement with the Assyrians.

"My mother, on the other hand, is determined that Nebiah marry a man who shares our faith in Jehovah God. My parents have left the final decision up to me!"

∽

4

THE KING IS DEAD

≈

I feared Jotham was about to be the bearer of bad news.

"You are my father's cousin and have always been my friend," he said. "My family has considered you a member of our family since we were children. The blood that courses through your veins is of royal heritage. Your love and loyalty for the king, as well as for me as his coregent, are without question.

"You have honored our family, and now we would like to honor you. I have informed my parents of my decision, and they have also granted their permission for you to marry my sister. And as your friend and regent, I am pleased to bring you the news."

I could not contain my joy! "You honor me, my sovereign and friend, with your great favor," I said. "You have brought joy to both Nebiah and me, and we thank you for this great kindness!"

. . .

Our union would accomplish two things for me. It would further solidify my position within the royal court of Judah. And most importantly, I would be marrying the woman I loved, who was also my best friend.

Six months later, our royal wedding took place at the palace. It was a joyful day filled with heartfelt wishes and blessings. Even King Uzziah attended – albeit from a distance. Screening was set up in one corner of the hall so he would not be visible to guests, but he could still hear all the festivities. Nebiah and I felt greatly blessed by Jehovah God as we retired for the evening.

Our bliss was shattered early the next morning, though, when one of the servants interrupted our sleep with the message: "King Uzziah is dead!"

Shock settled in as the family grappled with the news. We all knew the king's leprosy was getting worse, but none of us expected this. He was my king, my cousin – and now my father-in-law. I especially felt sorry for Jotham. He wasn't really given the opportunity to grieve his father's passing. Instead, he was immediately thrust into the singular role as king.

Though he had served as coregent, he had done so in the shadow of his father. Now that shadow was gone. The coregency had still been a part of his father's reign. Now Jotham would be weighed and assessed on his own merits.

Nebiah and I did our best to console one another, and together we attempted to console Queen Jerushah. But we all knew we needed to help the people of our kingdom mourn the passing of their king. We would need to grieve later. For now, we needed to remain strong.

A few nights after the king's death, I was experiencing a fitful night's sleep. All at once, I seemed to be in a crowd of people gathered in a magnificent temple. The building was far grander than anything I had ever seen, including the temple here in Jerusalem.

· · ·

It was also much larger. I could not see the walls opposite where I was standing. They were too far away for me to make them out. I turned to ask the people standing beside me where I was. But they were bowed on bent knees with arms uplifted.

At first I thought I was at a memorial gathering for King Uzziah. But then I began to hear what the crowd was saying. With one voice they were calling out, *"Holy, holy, holy is the Lord of Heaven's Armies! The whole earth is filled with His glory!"*[1]

I followed their gaze and could make out the shape of a throne in the distance. It was elevated high off the ground in what I presumed was the middle of the temple. Then I realized someone was seated on the throne.

As I watched, a host of what I now believe were angels encircled the throne. They were mighty men – larger than any I have ever seen. I've heard stories about the Philistine Goliath, but these men were even bigger than how he was described. And each of these men had six wings!

I was mesmerized as I watched them. With two of their wings, the angels were covering their faces. With two, they covered their feet, and with the remaining two they were flying around the throne.

They, too, were calling out, *"Holy, holy, holy is the Lord of Heaven's Armies! The whole earth is filled with His glory!"*[2]

However, the sound of their voices shook the temple to its very foundation. And soon the entire building began to fill with what looked like smoke.

It was then I realized who was seated on the throne. Somehow, I had entered the presence of Jehovah God, and it was the train of His robe filling the temple. I fell to my knees and cried out in fear.

∾

5

"HERE I AM. SEND ME."

~

"*It's all over!*" I cried out. "*I am doomed, for I am a sinful man. I have filthy lips, and I live among a people with filthy lips. Yet, I have seen the King, the Lord of Heaven's Armies.*"[1]

I could no longer look at the One on the throne. My body was weighed down by my sin. But soon I felt something hovering over me. With all my strength, I forced myself to look up. Flying above me was one of the angelic beings. He was holding a burning coal with a pair of tongs.

I suspected the coal had been taken from the burning altar that stood before the throne. He reached toward me with the coal. I tried to back away, but I could not move. He touched my lips with the coal, and as he did, he said: "*See, this coal has touched your lips. Now your guilt is removed, and your sins are forgiven.*"[2]

The weight I had felt was instantly gone. I looked at the One seated on the throne and heard Him say, "*Whom should I send as a messenger to this people? Who will go for Us?*"[3]

. . .

Immediately I rose to my feet and cried out, *"Here I am. Send me!"*[4]

My words echoed in my ears. Had I said them out loud? I must have ... because every eye in the room had now turned toward me – even the eyes of the Lord! *"Yes, go!"* the Lord said. *"But tell My people this: 'You will hear My words, but You will not understand. You will see what I do, but you will not perceive its meaning.'"*[5]

"Lord, how long must I do this?" I asked.[6]

"Until their cities are destroyed, with no one left in them," He answered. *"Until their houses are deserted and the whole country is an utter wasteland. Until I have sent everyone away to distant lands, and the entire land of Israel lies deserted. Even if only a remnant survives, like a tree that is cut down, the stump will be a holy seed that will grow again."*[7]

I knew I could not speak the words I was thinking. My heart was broken by God's promise of destruction. I wanted to shout, "No, Lord! Do not destroy our cities, our houses, and our nation!" I did not want to be the bearer of that news!

I looked at Him, and His eyes penetrated my soul. I began to panic. I wanted to flee from what He was telling me to do. But I knew I could not.

As much as I hated to hear those words, I knew God's punishment was just because of our sinful actions. And now, that same God was commanding me to deliver His message.

At that moment, I felt as if I were being swallowed by a giant whirlwind. I fell backward into a bottomless funnel. I grabbed wildly, trying to find something to hold on to, but to no avail. The whirlwind unexpectedly stopped, just as a familiar voice called out to me.

"Isaiah, what has come over you?" Nebiah asked. "Wake up, Isaiah!"

. . .

Gradually, I opened my eyes but was completely disoriented. I was covered in perspiration, and my heart was racing. I realized I was waking up from a dream. But was it a dream? It seemed so real!

I raised my fingers to feel the spot where the hot coal had touched my lips. I could still feel the sensation. It may have occurred in a dream, but I knew it was very real!

Nebiah's eyes were full of worry. "What is it, Isaiah?" she asked. "What's wrong? Were you having a dream?"

I paused for a moment to collect my thoughts. I sensed the Spirit of God helping me understand what had just taken place.

"Jehovah God has come to me in a dream!" I said. "Though I was asleep, the dream was real. He has chosen me to be His prophet. He has chosen me to tell His people what He is going to do!

"He has placed me in the palace – not to be a king – but to be a prophet to the kings. He has placed me among His people to be a prophet to His people. And I believe He has placed me among His people to tell them about a King who will reign over all kings when He comes one day!

"Nebiah, He has shown me I have been a man of unclean lips. But He has cleansed my lips and made them into an instrument He can use. He has shown me He already gave me visions even while your father was still alive. But I didn't have ears to hear or eyes to see them at the time. Neither did I have a cleansed mouth with which to repeat them. But now, all that has changed!"

～

6

COMPLETELY DEPENDENT
UPON GOD

❧

"The day is dawning," I declared, "and the time has come for me to stand before Jotham and our people and proclaim the Word of the Lord. Pray for me, Nebiah, that I will have the strength and the courage to say all that Jehovah God has told me to say."

I thought back to the day the prophet Amos delivered the Lord's message of judgment to Jotham. Little had I known then the impact that conversation would have on me now as I sought to walk in obedience to God.

Jotham had asked, "Amos, what can I do to appease God's wrath and lead our people to do what is right in His eyes?"

Amos had counseled Jotham to seek the Lord God Jehovah in all things. He was relentless in his opinion that our relationship with God, as His chosen people, was a moral contract. If we fail to honor the requirements of God's law, we cease to be in relationship with Him.

. . .

Amos also taught that our dependence on God is a requirement toward finding fulfillment in Him – personally and as a nation. He repeatedly told Jotham that apart from God, he would accomplish nothing.

He continued by reminding Jotham that our worship is not expressed to God through ceremonial actions; rather, it is demonstrated through genuine righteousness in our acts of service and justice.

Amos stood before Jotham and proclaimed, "The Lord showed me this vision. *I saw the Lord standing beside a wall that had been built using a plumb line. He was checking it with a plumb line to see if it was straight. And the Lord said to me, 'Amos, what do you see?'"*

"I answered, 'A plumb line.' And the Lord replied, 'I will test My people with this plumb line. I will no longer ignore all their sins.'"[(1)]

Amos may not have received his education in the school of the prophets, but every counselor and witness present in the hall – as well as the coregent himself – took note of this message. And I had been no exception. Even that day I sensed Jehovah God had positioned me in the Great Hall not for the wisdom I might speak, but so I might learn from what I heard and adjust my life to that same plumb line.

There was no question how God had used His prophet Amos to change the heart of Jotham. Since then, he had done much that was good and pleasing in the sight of the Lord. But, like his father, he had not destroyed the pagan shrines where many of our people continued to offer sacrifices and burn incense to false gods. And Amos had never failed to remind him of the plumb line.

I knew God had given Amos his message through a series of visions, similar to what I had just experienced. The king of Israel had rejected the message, but Jotham had not. Would my words as a prophet be rejected or received? I decided it was time for me to seek out Amos.

· · ·

When I arrived at his lodgings, he did not seem surprised to see me. Neither was he surprised to hear the account of my vision of the Lord.

"God chooses His servants," Amos said, "not based on their abilities but based on their availability. He called me from the pasture and you from the palace. But neither of us has received training from men. In that way, we are completely dependent upon God.

"As a prophet, your responsibility is saying everything God tells you to say. You cannot leave anything out or add anything to it. You will be responsible for communicating God's message – but you will not be responsible for how it is received.

"My greatest grief is seeing God's people rejecting God's Word. He does not permit me to rest until I have spoken the message He has given me. The burden is great, and the only thing that can ease it is delivering the words of the Lord.

"The Lord has also shown me, and I believe He has told me to tell you, 'Write down the words I give you. These words are not only for this current generation but also for the generations to come. Record my words so they can be passed from one generation to the next.'

"Further the Lord has said, '*One day I will restore the fallen house of David. I will repair its damaged walls. From the ruins I will rebuild it and restore its former glory. And Israel will possess what is left of Edom and all the nations I have called to be Mine.*'[(2)]

"The Lord has spoken, and He will do these things. The time will come! Be faithful, Isaiah. Do not shy away from what God has told you to do and say – for He will bring it all to pass at the right time."

"May God find me faithful in all He has told me to do and say," I responded as I prepared to return to the palace.

• • •

It was now time to tell my king the commission I had received from Jehovah God.

~

7

A KING REPENTS FOR HIS PEOPLE

∽

*T*he next morning, Jotham called to me as I entered the Great Hall. "Where were you yesterday, Isaiah?"

"I spent the day with the prophet Amos," I replied.

"What could you possibly have wanted to speak with him about?" he asked jokingly.

"I was in need of his counsel," I responded. "Something has happened I must tell you about. But I must speak to you not only as my king but also as my friend."

Jotham could see I was serious, so he immediately sent away the officials standing before him, and he motioned for me to take their place.

· · ·

"I hear the urgency in your voice, Isaiah," Jotham said empathetically. "I will listen to you as your friend and attempt to hear your words with the wisdom of a king. Tell me what has happened."

"The night before last," I began, "the Lord came to me in a dream – or rather, I entered into His presence while I was sleeping."

I then began to relay the events of my dream as clearly as I could recall them, not leaving out a single detail. Jotham never interrupted me but listened intently throughout my account. His expression became even more serious as I told him what God had said about the destruction of our cities, our houses, and our nation.

Then I told him, "I know I am not worthy to be the prophet of God on my own merits. But I also know He has placed this mantle upon me, and I can do no less. Hear the words I have told you, my friend – and my king – for thus has the Lord said."

Jotham did not speak at first. Rather, he stood to his feet and ripped his robe before falling to his knees. Then he cried out, "Forgive us, Oh God, for our transgressions against You! Forgive us – not because we deserve it – but because You are a merciful God. Forgive us for being a stiff-necked people who have rebelled against you from one generation to the next. Forgive us, and cleanse us of our wicked ways!

"Forgive me as the king of this people. In your sovereignty, You have placed me in authority over them. They will not turn to You with all their hearts if I do not do so. Lead me in the way that You would have me go that I might live in obedience to You!"

Jotham continued to cry out to God in repentance for the remainder of the morning. At first, those standing in the hall did not know what to do. But as Jotham continued to call out to God, they began to fall to their knees, one by one, crying out to God.

· · ·

By the time Jotham was done, everyone in the hall was on their knees and the sound of weeping echoed throughout the palace. Jotham turned his attention back to me and asked, "Oh man of God, what would Jehovah God have me do?"

"King Jotham," I replied, "He would have you seek Him and follow Him with all your heart, soul, mind, and strength. He would have you lead His people to obey His laws and all His precepts. You are to rebuild that which has been broken and cast out anyone who continues to rebel against Him. Thus has the Lord said!"

It was obvious Jotham intended to do just that. He had witnessed the downfall of his father due to his pride and had heard about the failures of his grandfather due to his disobedience. Jotham vowed to not repeat those failures but to follow the Lord completely.

He told me I was to stand before him each day in the Great Hall – no longer solely as a trustworthy friend – but now as the prophet of the Almighty God, ensuring Jehovah was honored through the king's every word and every action. From that day forward no one held a higher position of counsel to Jotham than I did.

The king knew the enemies of God and His people were a threat to the kingdom of Judah. The kings of the Ammonites, Aramites, and the northern kingdom of Israel continued to threaten further attack upon Jerusalem. Jotham knew the kingdom's defenses must be strengthened.

He completed the work begun by his father to rebuild the city gates and the defensive wall that overlooked the Kidron Valley. He assigned additional men and resources to the task so the work could be completed more quickly. But he knew that alone would not be enough.

~

8

BUT HE DID NOT DESTROY THE PAGAN SHRINES

~

*O*ver the next few years, Jotham led his people to establish new towns in the hill country of Judah so Jerusalem would no longer be isolated. He also led them to construct fortresses and watchtowers in the wooded areas surrounding the city. God granted him a reprieve from any enemy attacks while the defenses were being made ready.

But four years after King Uzziah died, Shanip (the king of Ammon) led his army to attack Jerusalem. Our people have a long history with the Ammonites. They are the descendants of Lot, the nephew of our patriarch Abraham. Long before the days of the exodus, Abraham permitted Lot to choose which land he and his offspring would inhabit. Lot chose the land on the east side of the Jordan River.

Almost 500 years had passed when God led our people to inhabit the Promised Land. He honored the agreement between Abraham and Lot, and instructed Moses: *"Do not bother the Ammonites, nor start a war with them. I have given the land of Ammon to them as their property, and I will not give you any of their land."*[1]

. . .

But over 400 years later, King Nahash of Ammon broke the agreement and threatened to attack some of the cities of Israel and enslave our people. King Saul led our people to defeat the Ammonites so devastatingly that it is written, *"Their army was so badly scattered that no two of them were left together."* [2] It was that victory that united our people from twelve individual tribes into the nation of Israel with Saul as our king.

Forty years after that, King Nahash's son, King Hanun, dishonored King David by disgracing his ambassadors and then foolishly sending their army to conquer Israel. But that army quickly retreated in defeat. Relations with the Ammonites remained quiet for 150 years until the reign of my ancestor King Jehoshaphat, at which time they formed an alliance with the Moabites to again threaten our people.

Those threats and a smattering of scattered skirmishes continued for the 100 years leading up to King Shanip's attack on Jerusalem. But because of Jotham's obedience, Jehovah God enabled Judah to regain its military strength, and the Ammonites were resoundingly defeated. Jotham was careful to give all the glory and honor to Jehovah God.

The Lord instructed me to tell Jotham to extract "an annual tribute of over 3 tons of silver, 50,000 bushels of wheat, and the same quantity of barley" from King Shanip for three years, which he did. The people took notice of Jehovah God's favor upon Jotham, and our surrounding neighbors also paid close heed to his growing power.

Judah prospered while the northern kingdom of Israel looked on with envy. The alliance between Pekah, the king of Israel, and Rezin, the king of the Arameans, continued and they made frequent threats against Jerusalem. But no such attacks occurred during the remainder of Jotham's reign.

Five years after Jotham became king, God blessed Nebiah and me with our firstborn son. God told me to name him Shear-jashub, which means "a remnant will return." He was to be a constant reminder to me of God's everlasting faithfulness to His people.

. . .

As Jotham's son, Ahaz, matured, the king would often have his son by his side so he could observe what it would be like to rule someday. I knew from when we were boys that Jotham had always regretted his father's decision not to include him in affairs of the kingdom. As a result, Jotham had been thrust into his position as coregent with very little preparation. He intended for his son to be better prepared.

But as I watched Ahaz, my spirit was troubled. Though he was still a boy, I did not see an earnestness in Ahaz to seek after God and honor Him. He seemed to be more taken by the luxuries of being king than he was with the solemn duty before God. I expressed my concerns to Jotham, but he dismissed them saying, "It is merely because my son is still a youth."

I feared that was not the case. I also reminded Jotham that he had not yet destroyed the pagan shrines where the people were still offering sacrifices and incense to their false gods. He assured me he was trying to lead the people to destroy the shrines on their own.

But I told him that left to their own devices the people would never choose to do so. I reminded him that his responsibility as their king was to lead them to honor God in ALL they did. Though Jotham aspired to obey God in all things, he failed to do so in this one way. He believed his personal example would be enough – but it was not. And I reminded him there are always consequences for sin.

One night, the Lord placed a song in my heart. My spirit was troubled, but I knew I must sing it to Jotham.

∾

9

CLOUDS HOVER OVER THE VINEYARD

~

*T*entered the Great Hall the next morning singing this song:

"My Beloved had a vineyard on a rich and fertile hill. He plowed the land, cleared its stones, and planted it with the best vines. In the middle He built a watchtower and carved a winepress in the nearby rocks. Then He waited for a harvest of sweet grapes, but the grapes that grew were bitter.

"Now, you people of Jerusalem and Judah, you judge between Me and My vineyard. What more could I have done for My vineyard that I have not already done? When I expected sweet grapes, why did My vineyard give Me bitter grapes?

"Now let Me tell you what I will do to My vineyard: I will tear down its hedges and let it be destroyed. I will break down its walls and let the animals trample it. I will make it a wild place where the vines are not pruned and the ground is not hoed, a place overgrown with briers and thorns. I will command the clouds to drop no rain on it."[1]

. . .

After I finished singing, I said, "Jotham, this is the story of the Lord's people. They are His vineyard. Israel and Judah are His pleasant garden. But there is judgment to come, and lest they repent and turn to Him, He will permit His people to be taken away into captivity. *Clouds hover over Israel and Judah, and one day soon they will blot out the light!*"[2]

Jotham became distraught. "Isaiah, are you telling me there is nothing I can do to stop it? Are you telling me that destruction and captivity will occur despite all I have done? I fear that our destruction will come from within the kingdom even more than it will come from outside the kingdom!"

There were already signs that forces were at work to remove Jotham from the throne. Several advisors who had served his father were expressing concern about the growing alliance between the northern kingdom and the Arameans. They had encouraged Uzziah to enter an alliance with the Assyrians, but now they were suggesting Jotham pay tribute to the Assyrian king and give him control over the defenses of our kingdom.

Few in the palace were concerned about hearing from God or following His direction; most were ready to follow the might of the Assyrians. My voice of reason was carrying less weight in the Great Hall. Yes, I feared destruction and captivity would come all too soon.

I also began to observe those same counselors who were attempting to lead Jotham closer to the Assyrians had now gained the ear of Ahaz. Each day I saw the twenty-year-old heir to the throne being drawn more and more to them and away from his father.

One afternoon Nebiah told me she feared for her brother's safety. She had heard rumors that a pro-Assyrian faction now felt so emboldened they were making plans to force Jotham off the throne. No matter how much she or I tried to warn him, he disregarded our concerns.

A week later, I arrived early one morning at the Great Hall. I hoped to speak with Jotham before the others arrived. I saw him kneeling beside the throne – which was not an unusual sight. I hesitated to interrupt his prayer time, but I knew it was urgent that we speak.

I stood at a respectful distance from the throne and said, "Your majesty, please forgive my intrusion, but I have come to speak with you about a matter of urgency."

I waited a few minutes for him to respond. I presumed he was concluding his prayer time before he answered me. But after considerable time had passed, he still did not acknowledge me.

I walked closer and knelt beside him as if to join him in prayer. When I placed my hand on his shoulder, his body fell forward onto the floor. It was then I saw the hilt of a knife protruding from his chest and his blood-soaked clothing.

His eyes and mouth were open, but he wasn't making a sound. He was no longer breathing. My king, and my friend, was dead!

I called out for help. Within moments, the guards stationed at the outer doors came running. Over the next several hours, I felt like I was falling in the whirlwind from my dream. But this time, it was no dream. King Jotham had been murdered – and everything seemed out of control!

Soon, Queen Ahio and Ahaz arrived. Ahaz was no longer the prince; he was now the king. I watched as he consoled his mother in her grief, but I saw little, if any, sorrow in my nephew. No one seemed to know who had committed this act of treachery. But I feared Ahaz knew only too well.

Funeral arrangements were made. Our new king ascended to the throne. Life in the palace changed. Life in Judah soon changed. The grapes in the vineyard of Judah had just become more bitter!

∾

10

MAHER-SHALAL-HASH-BAZ

~

*T*he days of mourning for King Jotham had not yet been completed when we learned an army from the north was approaching to lay siege to Jerusalem. King Rezin of Aram and King Pekah of the northern kingdom had apparently determined that Judah would be most vulnerable at this moment.

The army was only two days away from reaching our city. Those of us who gave counsel to the king were divided on what we should do. Those who had advised Jotham to call on Assyrian King Tiglath-Pileser III for protection were now urging Ahaz to quickly do the same. I felt I needed to remind Ahaz their protection would come at a price.

I knew he would be surveying the defenses of the city's water supply to make certain it was adequately secured before the attack. I decided to meet him there so we could talk without the interference of competing voices. I brought my son with me at the Lord's prompting. Ahaz had always been fond of his younger cousin.

• • •

"Your majesty," I began, "the Assyrians would be only too happy to make Judah a part of their growing empire and you a puppet king under the rule of a man who does not fear Jehovah God. Rather, we must turn to the Lord and trust Him to defend us against Israel and Aram.

"Jehovah God has said, '*You do not need to fear the fierce anger of those two burned-out embers, King Rezin and King Pekah.* Yes, they are threatening to invade and install another to replace you as king. But this is what I say: *This invasion will never happen!*'"[1]

Ahaz looked at me in silence as he pondered his decision. "We will do as the Lord has said," he finally replied. "Our fighting men will defend our city and trust Him for the victory – because there is not enough time for me to do anything different."

Amazingly, despite Ahaz's obvious lack of faith, God granted us the victory, and our city withstood the attack. Our enemies retreated to their lands until what I expected would be another day. But instead of rejoicing in the victory God had given us, Ahaz continued to turn away from Him.

Not long after that day, the Lord sent me back to Ahaz with this message: "*Ask Me for a sign to prove that I will crush your enemies as I have promised. Ask for anything you like and make it as difficult as you want.*"[2]

But Ahaz refused, saying: "*No, I wouldn't test the Lord like that.*[3]

"All right, then," I replied, "the Lord Himself has chosen the sign. *Look! The virgin will conceive a Child! She will give birth to a son and will call Him Immanuel, meaning 'God is with us.'*[4]

"But before this child is born, *the Lord will bring a terrible curse on you, your nation and your family. You will soon experience greater terror than has been known in all the years since Solomon's empire was divided. The Lord will take the 'razor' – the Assyrians you seek to protect you – and use it to shave off everything: your land, your crops, and your people.*[5]

. . .

"When they finally stop plundering, few people will be left. The entire land will be one vast brier patch, covered by briers and thorns."[(6)]

I prayed those words would bring Ahaz to repentance, but instead his heart was hardened. He did not receive the word of the Lord. Rather, he did what was right in his own eyes and abandoned all his father had done. Instead of following his father's example, he followed the example of the kings of Israel.

My heart was uplifted by the Lord's promise of the child who would one day be born! But I was heartbroken over the destruction that would first come to my people, my nation, and my family. Ahaz was part of my family. The offspring of Solomon were a part of my family – and all would come under the judgment that God had just declared through me. I looked into the hardness of Ahaz's eyes, and my heart broke even more.

In the days immediately following, Ahaz discharged all the counselors who had loyally served his father – including me. As a member of the royal family, I continued to live in the palace, but I was no longer a part of the king's trusted circle. But Ahaz's insult would not change the fact I am the prophet of the Most High God, and I will bear His message wherever, whenever, and to whomever He chooses.

A short time later, my wife gave birth to our second son, whom the Lord told me to name Maher-shalal-hash-baz, which means "he has made haste to the plunder." God told me that before my son was old enough to call me "papa," the king of Assyria would invade the northern kingdom and carry away their riches.

The Lord sent me back to Ahaz to declare His words:

"Do not think like everyone else does. Do not be afraid that some plan conceived behind closed doors will be the end of you. Do not fear anything except the Lord

Almighty. He alone is the Holy One. If you fear Him, you need fear nothing else. But if you do not, there will be trouble and anguish and dark despair."[7]

However, Ahaz still did not heed the words of the Lord.

~

11

A SON IS BORN TO A FOOLISH KING

~

*T*he announcement of an upcoming birth brings hope to every home – including a palace. King Ahaz proudly proclaimed that his wife, Queen Abijah, was with child. He spoke with great certainty that the child would be a son. The happy news was a welcome relief from the many challenges our kingdom was facing.

Ahaz seemed grateful that he was being congratulated for something. I will confess it was the first positive word I had been able to speak to him since he became king.

He had wasted no time in bringing the images of Baal, which Jehoiada the priest had destroyed one hundred years earlier, back into our kingdom. He seemed intent on following the examples of the disobedient kings of the northern kingdom instead of following the examples set by his father and grandfather.

He reintroduced the detestable practices of the pagan nations the Lord had driven out of the land ahead of His people under Joshua's leadership.

Ahaz offered sacrifices – both animal and human – and burned incense at the pagan shrines Jotham had failed to destroy.

The destruction God had said would come to pass was now beginning to take place. The king of Edom declared war on Judah to recover the town of Elath in the southern part of our kingdom. Edom prevailed and the town Ahaz's grandfather, Uzziah, had rebuilt was lost.

Edom's victory emboldened the Philistine king to raid the towns of Judah located in the foothills along the Negev. They captured and were now occupying six of those villages. King Rezin and King Pekah clearly saw God had withdrawn His hand of protection from Judah, prompting them to redeploy their armies to attack Jericho.

In a single day, King Pekah's army killed 120,000 of our fighting men. Elkanah, Ahaz's second in command, and Azrikam, the king's palace commander, were both killed in that devastating attack. Also, 200,000 women and children were captured by the armies of Israel and taken into exile to Samaria.

Amazingly, they chose not to advance on Jerusalem. Their goal had apparently been to humiliate Ahaz, not kill him. They knew the former would be more painful than the latter.

Even with all that carnage, Ahaz rejected my pleas for him to repent and turn to Jehovah God. But the pagan armies of Israel apparently feared God more than the king of Judah!

When the armies of Israel returned to Samaria, they were met by a prophet of the Lord named Oded. He told them: *"The Lord, the God of your ancestors, was angry with Judah and let you defeat them. But you have gone too far, and all heaven is disturbed! Listen to me and return these captives you have taken, for they are your own relatives. Watch out, because now the Lord's fierce anger has been turned against you!"* [1]

. . .

Having heard Oded, some of the leaders of Israel also turned to the armies and said, "*You must not bring the prisoners here! We cannot afford to add to our sins and guilt – or the Lord's fierce anger will be turned against us even more.*"[2]

So, to our surprise, they returned the captives to Jericho. They provided them with clothing, sandals, and food from the looting they had seized. Those who were too weak to walk were placed on the backs of donkeys.

As I entered the Great Hall, I cried out, "King Ahaz, there is no question God has been merciful and gracious to the people – and to you! Surely you must see that! Turn from your wicked ways and turn to Him!"

But again, Ahaz hardened his heart. Instead of turning to God, he turned to the king of Assyria, sending him this message: "*I am your servant and your vassal. Come up and rescue me from the attacking armies of Aram and Israel.*"[3]

King Tiglath-pileser agreed to do so – but when he arrived in Jerusalem, he came not as a friend or a helper but as a conqueror. Jerusalem had been given into his hands without any resistance.

Ahaz soon realized his error, but his attempted solution was to barter his way out of his mistake. He collected silver and gold from the Lord's temple, the palace, and the homes of all his officials and presented it to the king of Assyria in hopes he would receive it as a gift. Even King Tiglath-pileser looked at Ahaz with disbelief – how could this king be so foolish and naïve?

From another room in the palace, I heard a baby's cry. Ahaz's son, Hezekiah, had just entered the world.

∾

12

AN ABOMINATION

~

*K*ing Tiglath-pileser attacked the Aramean capital of Damascus, ostensibly to defend Judah. But truth be told, the king of Assyria had already planned to attack Aram for his own personal gain. Now he was being doubly rewarded to do so! The Assyrian army killed King Rezin and led the defeated Aramean soldiers away as captives.

The Aramean women and children did not share the soldiers' fate. Instead, they remained captives in Damascus serving under the brutality of their Assyrian masters. King Tiglath-pileser chose to temporarily remain in that city. From there, he sent word to Ahaz to come to him, demanding that he bring additional payment.

Ahaz swore his allegiance to the Assyrian king after arriving in Damascus. He began to take great pleasure in the things he saw around the city. Ahaz particularly admired an altar used to worship Baal. He had a model of the altar made, together with plans detailing its design, and sent them to one of his priests in Jerusalem with instructions to have the altar built and ready for him when he returned.

. . .

Meanwhile, Ahaz's son was now becoming a young lad. He favored his grandfather, Jotham, in appearance and temperament, much more than he did his father. Hezekiah's mother, Queen Abijah, permitted me to spend more and more time with the boy. Although Ahaz no longer listened to a word I said, God was allowing me to be a mentor to Hezekiah.

The Lord showed me He would rebuild Judah through Hezekiah. I was to teach the boy about the laws and ways of Jehovah God. And the young prince, for his part, demonstrated an insatiable thirst to learn and understand.

Queen Abijah subsequently gave birth to two additional sons – the older was named Manasseh and the younger boy named Tiglath in honor of the Assyrian king. Sadly, neither child lived long enough for me to teach them the ways of God.

When Ahaz returned to Jerusalem, he immediately went to look for the altar he had commissioned to be built. After it passed his inspection, the altar was placed in front of the Lord's temple. He then sent word to have his son, Manasseh, brought to him. Ahaz wrapped his arm around his son and proudly showed him the altar as they walked around it. The lad had never received such attention from his father. He was clearly relishing the moment.

But then the mood abruptly changed. Ahaz tied his son's hands and feet, and placed him on the altar. Witnesses gasped in horror. The priests of Baal began to move about the altar, as if they were in a trance, making groaning sounds that seemed to rise from the very pit of hell.

My son, Shear-jashub, ran to where I was teaching Hezekiah and told me what Ahaz was doing. I immediately ran as quickly as I could to try and stop him – but I was too late. Ahaz had slit his son's throat moments before I arrived. The priests of Baal were gathering the boy's blood into basins. I had never witnessed such an abomination!

• • •

"Ahaz, stop! What have you done?" I cried out. "You have murdered your innocent son! You have profaned Jehovah God! You have desecrated His temple! Does nothing good remain within you?"

I knew I could have been executed for speaking to my king that way, but I did not care. I could not stand by silently and not charge him for his evil actions. But he never reacted. He just stood there over his lifeless son, staring blankly into the distance, while the worshipers of Baal continued to cry out around him.

The consequences for my outburst were swift. Members of the palace guard quickly ushered me away. Soon I was informed my family and I were no longer welcome at the palace. We must find other lodging immediately, and I was no longer permitted in the king's hall. I didn't really care because I did not want my family exposed to such an evil king – nor did I want us living under his roof.

I went to our rooms to tell my wife we must pack our belongings; but first, I pulled my family around me. Nebiah was holding our daughter, Hephzibah, who had been born only a few months earlier. I hugged them tightly, together with my sons, Shear-jashub and Maher-shalal-hash-baz, as I cried out to God to deliver His people from this evil king.

As we were leaving the palace, I received a message from Queen Abijah asking if I would continue to teach Hezekiah. She would find a way for me to do so in secret. I knew this was what the Lord wanted, so I sent word back that I would.

~

13

A SON IS PROMISED, AND A KING DIES

~

*A*s the days passed, Ahaz ran out of treasures to present to the Assyrian king as tribute. Instead, he embraced the gods of the Assyrians to gain favor with the ruler. But nothing he did seemed to help.

Ahaz became increasingly desperate. He led the people of Judah to abandon the worship of Jehovah God and turn to the pagan gods. He shut the doors of the Lord's temple so no one could worship there. He took the few remaining utensils of worship from the temple and broke them into pieces.

He then set up altars to the pagan gods in every corner of Jerusalem and throughout Judah. Just when it looked as if he could do no worse, he took his son Tiglath to the Valley of Hinnom, on the western side of the city, and sacrificed him in the fire.

Days became weeks, weeks became months, and months became years. I cried out to God to stop Ahaz's madness, and yet it continued. Hunger and misery spread throughout the land, but instead of turning to God, the people shook their fists at Him and cursed Him.

. . .

One bright exception was Hezekiah. As he grew in stature, he grew in knowledge and dedication to the Lord – despite the actions of his father. He listened intently as I told him all the Lord was promising would come to pass.

"The Lord has told me to write down all these things as a testimony of what all He will do. The time of darkness and despair will not go on forever. The people who walk in darkness will see a great light – a light that will shine on all who live in the land where death casts its shadow.[1]

"God will break the chains that bind His people and the whip that scourges them, just as He did in the days of Moses. But on that day *a Child will be born to us, a Son will be given. And the government will rest on His shoulders. These will be His royal titles: Wonderful Counselor, Mighty God, Everlasting Father, Prince of Peace.*[2]

"His ever expanding, peaceful government will never end. He will rule forever with fairness and justice from the throne of His ancestor David. The passionate commitment of the Lord Almighty will guarantee this!"[3]

"Isaiah, when will this come to pass?" Hezekiah asked.

"Destruction is certain before the coming of the Promised One," I replied. *The Lord's fist is poised to strike. He will send desolation upon Israel and Judah from a distant land. The Lord says: 'Assyria is the whip of My anger. Its military power is a club in My hand.*[4] *Assyria will enslave My people. It will plunder them, trampling them like dirt beneath its feet. But the king of Assyria will not know that it is I who sent him. He will merely think he is attacking My people as part of his plan to conquer the world.'*[5]

"After the Lord has used the king of Assyria to accomplish His purposes in Jerusalem, He will turn against him and punish him for his arrogance. He will completely destroy Assyria's warriors. Only a few will survive – so few that a child could count them![6]

. . .

"Then at last those left in Israel and Judah will trust the Lord, the Holy One of Israel. They will no longer depend on the Assyrians, who would destroy them. A remnant of them will return. Though the people of Israel are as numerous as the sand on the seashore, only a few of them will return.[7]

"The Lord Almighty says: 'My people in Jerusalem, do not be afraid of the Assyrians when they oppress you just as the Egyptians did long ago. It will not last very long. In a little while My anger against you will end, and then My anger will rise up to destroy them. I will cut them down as an ax cuts down the forest trees in Lebanon.'[8]

"Out of the stump of David's family – your family, Hezekiah – *will grow a shoot* – *yes, a new Branch bearing fruit from the old root. In that day the wolf and the lamb will live together, the leopard and the goat will be at peace. Calves and yearlings will be safe from lions, and a little child will lead them all."*[9]

"Will this occur in my lifetime?" the young prince asked.

"Only Jehovah God knows when these events will unfold," I answered, "and His Promised One will come. In the meantime, we are to honor Him and follow Him with all our hearts, souls, minds, and strength. When you become king, you must do everything you can to lead the people to do the same."

"I will remember His promise," Hezekiah declared, "and I will seek to honor and follow Him in all I do!"

God mercifully limited Ahaz's days. When the Lord determined Hezekiah was ready to become king, Ahaz died. No one was ever able to explain what caused his death. But on that day, it felt like a great cloud had been lifted off Judah.

≈

14

THE TEMPLE IS RESTORED

~

*K*ing Hezekiah wasted no time in undoing the evil practices put in place by his father. He had all the pagan shrines and altars removed and destroyed. He smashed the pillars that had been erected for pagan worship, including the Asherah poles.

He even destroyed the bronze serpent Moses had made because the people had turned it into an object of worship. Within the first month of his reign, he reopened the doors of the temple of the Lord and repaired them. He summoned the priests and Levites to meet with him at the courtyard on the east side of the temple.

Hezekiah proclaimed, *"Listen to me, you Levites! Purify yourselves, and purify the temple of the Lord, the God of your ancestors. Remove all the defiled things from the sanctuary. Our ancestors were unfaithful and did what was evil in the sight of the Lord our God.*[1]

"They abandoned the Lord and His temple; they turned their backs on Him. That is why the Lord's anger has fallen upon Judah and Jerusalem. He has made us an object of dread, horror, and ridicule, as you can so plainly see.[2]

. . .

"But now I will make a covenant with the Lord, the God of Israel, so that His fierce anger will turn away from us. My dear Levites, do not neglect your duties any longer! The Lord has chosen you to stand in His presence, to minister to Him, and to lead the people in worship and make offerings to Him."[3]

The Levites got right to work. They purified themselves and began the work to cleanse the temple. They carefully followed the instructions handed down from the Lord through King Solomon. They removed all the defiled things and had them burned in the Kidron Valley.

It took sixteen days before they were able to report back to Hezekiah: "We have purified the temple, the altar of burnt offering, and the table of Show-bread pointing to the presence of God. We have purified all the utensils, including those taken by King Ahaz. Everything is now cleansed and ready for use."

Early the next morning, Hezekiah instructed the city officials to gather at the temple and bring seven bulls, seven rams, seven lambs, and seven male goats to be given as a sin offering. He commanded the priests, who were descendants of Aaron, to sacrifice the animals on the altar of the Lord.

They killed the animals and sprinkled the blood on the altar to make atonement for the sins of all of Israel. Hezekiah stationed the Levites throughout the temple with trumpets, cymbals, harps, and lyres to lead the people in songs of praise and worship from the psalms of David.

When the dedication of the temple was completed, Hezekiah instructed all the people to bring their sacrifices and offerings to be presented to the Lord. But there were too few priests to accept all the offerings, so Hezekiah directed the Levites to help them.

. . .

Every element of pagan worship, including the high places, was destroyed and the temple of the Lord was restored. The people rejoiced because of what God had accomplished so quickly.

Hezekiah then invited everyone throughout Israel and Judah to come to the temple in Jerusalem to celebrate the Passover. His messengers carried letters that read: "Oh people of Israel, return to the Lord. Do not be like your ancestors and relatives who abandoned the Lord and became an object of ridicule. Come to His temple, which He has set apart as holy forever.

"Worship Him so that His fierce anger will turn away from you. For the Lord your God is gracious and merciful. If you return to Him, He will not continue to turn His face from you."[4]

When the people came together, everyone celebrated joyfully for two weeks. Jerusalem had not seen a celebration like this one since the days of King Solomon. God heard the praises of His people from His holy dwelling in heaven. Hezekiah wholeheartedly did what was pleasing and good in the sight of the Lord ... and God rewarded His efforts.

~

15

THE DAYS OF PROSPERITY UNDER HEZEKIAH'S REIGN

~

*T*he day Hezekiah became king, he arranged for me and my family to move back into the palace. He told me he wanted me close by his side. His mother had preserved our accommodations during our absence and embraced us warmly upon our return.

Hezekiah also immediately restored my position as chief counselor to the king. Though I knew that role would always be secondary to God's call on my life to be His prophet, I was grateful to again have free access to the king and to be a voice of godly wisdom for him. Hezekiah dismissed all those who had served his father and surrounded himself with men who earnestly sought to honor the Lord God Jehovah.

After the celebration at the temple, the king organized the priests and Levites into divisions to present the offerings of the people and lead them in giving thanksgiving and praise to the Lord. The king made a personal contribution from his royal flocks and herds for the daily burnt offerings, as well as for the weekly Sabbath festival.

. . .

In turn, he required the people to bring a portion of their income, as prescribed by the Mosaic laws, to the priests and Levites so they could devote themselves fully to the law of the Lord. The people responded with overwhelming generosity, so Hezekiah directed that storerooms be built in the temple to safeguard their gifts.

The people's offerings and the distribution to the priests and Levites were done in a way that honored God. And He, in turn, rewarded Hezekiah and the people for their faithfulness.

The year after Ahaz died, the Lord gave me this message for the Philistines: "*Do not rejoice, you Philistines, that the king who attacked you is dead. For even though that whip is broken, his son will be worse than his father ever was. I will wipe you out with famine.*

"*I will destroy the few who remain. A powerful army is coming against you from the north.*[(1)] And it is the Lord who comes before them."

Hearing this word from the Lord, Hezekiah dispatched his army to attack the Philistines starting in the foothills along the Negev. The army of Judah quickly recaptured the six villages seized by the Philistines during Ahaz's reign. Our army then proceeded into Gaza and conquered the remainder of their territory – from their smallest outpost to their largest walled city. The Lord had truly gone before them.

In the fourth year of Hezekiah's reign, the king of Assyria attacked the kingdom of Israel to the north and began a siege on the city of Samaria – just as the Lord had shown me would happen. Despite everything the kings of Israel had seen God do on Hezekiah's behalf, they continued to dishonor God and violate His covenant. The siege lasted for three years until Samaria fell. The Assyrian king deported all the Israelites and scattered them in colonies to multiple cities within Assyria. Through it all, Judah remained unthreatened and unharmed.

As a matter of fact, throughout the first thirteen years of his reign, Hezekiah experienced great blessings from the Lord. The region of Judah expanded, the people were prosperous, the king's treasury and the temple storehouse continued to grow in bounty and riches. It appeared that God's wrath had been turned away from Judah – at least during the reign of this king.

I couldn't have been prouder of my king and his dedication to the Lord if he were my own son. In many respects, I loved him like one of my own sons. Never once did he turn a deaf ear to the messages I brought him from the Lord, and never did he ignore my counsel.

So I was overjoyed when he asked for my blessing on his intended marriage to my daughter, Hephzibah. His request did not come as a surprise. Nebiah and I had been witnessing this developing relationship between them for some time. We knew it would be a marriage of complementing strengths, of mutual love and respect, and of shared passion to honor the Lord in all things.

There was a huge celebration throughout the kingdom on Hezekiah and Hephzibah's wedding day. There was no question in anyone's mind that God was again showering His blessings on our king and the kingdom. And I thanked the Lord for one additional role He had granted me – to be the father-in-law of the king I loved so dearly.

For a while it seemed as if nothing could go wrong – our days were filled with joy. But during the fourteenth year of Hezekiah's reign, the armies of King Sennacherib of Assyria came to attack Judah.

∽

16

PREPARING FOR AN ASSYRIAN INVASION

❦

*W*hile Ahaz was king, Judah's wealth and resources were depleted because of the offerings demanded by the king of Assyria. An empty treasury held little interest for subsequent rulers of Assyria. So Judah was left alone, despite the fact the Assyrians controlled the regions surrounding the kingdom.

Hezekiah had no intention of making payments, but he knew Assyria would not ignore Judah forever. So, he sought an alliance with Sidon, Ascalon, Ekron, and Egypt in hopes that together they could keep the Assyrians at bay. Once King Sennacherib learned of this rebel alliance, however, he set out to destroy it.

He dispatched his army to attack Ascalon, followed by Sidon, and then Ekron. Each domain fell and was absorbed into the Assyrian kingdom. By that point, the alliance had broken down and everyone was left to fend for themselves. Sennacherib next turned his attention toward Judah. He knew Jerusalem was the most fortified city of the kingdom, so he began by attacking the other cities.

. . .

One by one, the cities of Judah were defeated by Assyria's military. Hezekiah knew once the fortified cities fell, Sennacherib would target Jerusalem. And if Jerusalem fell, all would be lost. Judah would be conquered, and our people would be scattered as captives into Assyrian cities.

Hezekiah consulted with officials and his military advisers and determined Jerusalem would not survive a prolonged siege. He needed to buy enough time to strengthen the city's defenses. I, together with the rest of his counselors, advised Hezekiah to give the Assyrian king an offering in order to buy the needed time.

The Assyrian forces had just captured the city of Lachish, and Sennacherib had temporarily taken up residence there. Hezekiah sent the king a message, apologizing for his failure to make payments, saying it was a disrespectful expression of rebellion on his part.

Hezekiah hoped his offer to resume sending tribute would diminish Sennacherib's thirst to conquer Judah and cause him to turn back – or at least slow his advance toward Jerusalem. Hezekiah's message read: "To the honorable king of Assyria, *I have done wrong. I will pay whatever tribute money you demand if you will only go away.*"[1]

The Assyrian king sent back a message to Hezekiah with his demand: "I will accept no less than ten tons of silver, and one ton of gold."[2]

Though the demand was outrageous, we all advised Hezekiah to make the payment. All the silver stored in the temple of the Lord and in the palace treasury was gathered. Even the gold inlaid on the doors and doorposts of the temple was stripped so we could meet the king's demand. Twenty-two oxen-drawn carts, protected by 1,000 of our fighting men, traveled for two days to deliver the silver and gold to the king.

But even before the oxen departed Jerusalem, Hezekiah ordered repairs to begin on the wall of the city. Once that was finished, construction on a second wall outside of the first was completed. The king also ordered the defensive terraces surrounding the City of David be reinforced.

Hezekiah knew one of our greatest vulnerabilities was our water supply, which comes from the Gihon Spring. The spring originates at the base of the hill on which the City of David is built. The spring's waters emerge from a cave, which in turn acts as a siphon on the eastern side of the city and, at the time, flowed from there into Jerusalem through channels in the Kidron Valley.

Knowing the Assyrians could easily dam the channels – leaving us with no access to water – Hezekiah redirected the water flow by building an underground tunnel beneath the City of David leading from the spring to a pool inside the walls of Jerusalem. It was an amazing engineering feat.

Two teams, starting at opposite ends and working toward the middle, began excavation of the 533-meter tunnel. It took four years to complete, which in the providence of Jehovah God, coincided with the time Sennacherib began his attacks on our fortified cities.

Once Hezekiah became aware that an Assyrian attack was imminent, he directed the above-ground access be capped off. Not only did this protect our water supply, but it also diminished the water available to the Assyrian forces.

Countless workers began manufacturing weapons and shields so all our people would be equipped for battle. Shifts worked around the clock – except on the Sabbath – until all the preparations were completed.

∿

17

THE ASSYRIAN KING MOCKS THE
LORD GOD

~

*H*ezekiah called all the people of Jerusalem to gather in the square at the city gate. He knew they were anxious because they had heard what the Assyrians had done to the people in the cities they had conquered.

The king offered them this encouragement: *"Be strong and courageous! Don't be afraid of the king of Assyria or his mighty army, for there is a power far greater on our side! The Assyrian king may have a great army, but they are just men. We have the Lord our God to help us and to fight our battles for us!"*[1]

The people calmed down – until they saw the mighty Assyrian army approaching from the south. They watched as a large fighting force, led by Assyrian General Rab-shakeh, made camp on the horizon just outside the City of David.

We soon learned Sennacherib was not with them. He was planning to march on the city of Libnah with another portion of his army before meeting up with Rab-shakeh here in Jerusalem. He had sent this force to

camp outside our walls to intimidate us. It wasn't long before Rab-shakeh
approached our city gate. He shouted so all the people could hear.

"I am General Rab-shakeh, personal representative of the great king of
Assyria! *This is what our great king says to Hezekiah, king of Judah: 'What are
you trusting in that makes you so confident? Do you think that mere words can
substitute for military skill and strength? Which of your military allies will give
you any backing against Assyria? Will Egypt? If you lean on Egypt, you will find
it to be a stick that breaks into pieces. The pharaoh of Egypt is completely unreli-
able!*[(2)]

"'*But perhaps you will say that you are trusting in the Lord your God. Surely you
must realize what I and the other kings of Assyria before me have done to all the
people of the earth! Were any of their gods able to rescue them from my power?
Name just one time when any god anywhere was able to rescue his people from
me!*[(3)]

"'*People of Judah, do not let Hezekiah fool you! Don't let him deceive you like this!
I say it again – no god of any nation has ever yet been able to rescue his people
from me or my ancestors. How much less will your God rescue you from my
power!*'"[(4)]

The general continued to mock the Lord God Jehovah and His servant
Hezekiah by heaping one insult after another. Rab-shakeh spoke about our
God in heaven as if He were one of the pagan gods made by human
hands.

"King Hezekiah," General Rab-shakeh called out, "*I'll tell you what! My
master, the king of Assyria, has said, 'I will strike a bargain with you. If you can
find two thousand horsemen in your entire army, I will give you two thousand
horses for them to ride on! With your tiny army, how can you think of challenging
even the weakest contingent of my troops?*'"[(5)]

"*People of Judah, don't listen to Hezekiah! This is what my king is offering to you:
'Make peace with me – open the gates and come out. Then I will allow each of you
to continue eating from your own garden and drinking from your own well. Then*

I will arrange to take you to another land like this one – a country with bountiful harvests of grain and wine, bread and vineyards, olive trees and honey – a land of plenty. Choose life instead of death!'" [(6)]

When the general finished, he returned to the Assyrian camp. Our people silently waited for their king to respond. Hezekiah tore his clothes, put on sackcloth, and entered the temple of the Lord to pray.

Before doing so, he sent me this message: "Isaiah, *this is a day of trouble, insult, and disgrace. It is like when a child is ready to be born, but the mother has no strength to deliver it. But perhaps the Lord our God has heard the words of the Assyrian messenger defying* Him and blaspheming His name. What would the Lord God have me say to the Assyrians?" [(7)]

The Lord had already given me His reply.

"King Hezekiah, *this is what the Lord says: 'Do not be disturbed by the blasphemous speech against Me from the Assyrian king's messenger. Listen! I Myself will make sure that the king will receive a report from Assyria telling him that he is needed at home. Then I will make him want to return to his land, where I will have him killed with a sword.'"* [(8)]

For the next several days, the Assyrian army remained in their encampment making their preparations to attack us – and we waited on our God!

~

18

THE LORD GOD JEHOVAH WILL NOT BE MOCKED

～

A few days later, as the morning sun rose, our lookouts brought word the Assyrian army was gone. They had left in the middle of the night. People across the city began to shout with joy. Praises to God for His deliverance poured from their lips – but their jubilation was short-lived.

Later that morning, Hezekiah's spies reported that General Rab-shakeh had only withdrawn his troops temporarily. The general had received word the army led by King Sennacherib was being attacked by the king of Egypt. Rab-shakeh's army had gone to assist in the fight.

Hezekiah received a letter around midday from Sennacherib's general that read: "Do not be deceived into thinking I have withdrawn in defeat. I will return – and when I do, it will be with my full force!"

The next day the Lord gave me this message He had spoken against the Assyrian king: *"Whom have you been defying and ridiculing? Against whom did you raise your voice? At whom did you look with such haughty eyes? It was the Holy One of Israel!*

. . .

"By your messengers you have defied the Lord. You have said, 'With my many chariots I have conquered the highest mountains – yes, the remotest peaks of Lebanon. I have cut down its tallest cedars and its finest cypress trees. I have reached its farthest heights and explored its deepest forests. I have dug wells in many foreign lands and refreshed myself with their water. With the sole of my foot, I stopped up all the rivers of Egypt!'

"But have you not heard? I decided this long ago. Long ago I planned it, and now I am making it happen. I planned for you to crush fortified cities into heaps of rubble.

That is why their people have so little power and are so frightened and confused. They are as weak as grass, as easily trampled as tender green shoots.

"But I know you well – where you stay and when you come and go. I know the way you have raged against Me. And because of your raging against Me and your arrogance, which I have heard for Myself, I will put My hook in your nose and My bit in your mouth. I will make you return by the same road on which you came."[1]

Immediately, I went to the Great Hall to find Hezekiah and tell him what the Lord said.

Several weeks later, the Assyrian forces reappeared on the horizon outside the City of David. But this time, it was the combined forces of the Assyrian army, fresh on the heels of their defeat of the Egyptian army.

Again, I went before Hezekiah and brought him this message: *"This is what the Lord says about the king of Assyria: 'His armies will not enter Jerusalem to shoot their arrows. They will not march outside its gates with their shields or build banks of earth against its walls. The king will not enter this city. For My own honor and for the sake of My servant David, I will defend it.'"*[2]

. . .

Hezekiah sent word to all the people: "Watch and see the deliverance of the Lord!"

Throughout the night, Hezekiah remained in the temple of the Lord praying for the deliverance of his people. Little did he, or anyone else, know what the Lord was doing as many of us joined him in prayer.

As the sun rose, we heard shouts from the Assyrian camp. But they were not shouts of war – they were shouts of confusion! About 185,000 soldiers had come down with a plague overnight and were dead. The handful remaining were surrounded by dead corpses. Fear and panic spread throughout their camp.

We watched as Sennacherib, Rab-shakeh, and the few remaining officers tried to bring order to their greatly reduced ranks. But even from a distance we could tell they were all afraid. Within minutes, the order was given to break camp and quickly depart to the south. They didn't even take time to bury their dead.

Shouts of joy again broke out across the city. Hezekiah led us in a week-long season of praise and thanksgiving before our God. As always, He had been true to His Word. He had defended our city and defeated our enemy, and we didn't raise a hand. All glory and honor were due Him – and Him alone!

Never again was Hezekiah threatened by the Assyrians. God had fought for us. Many years later, I learned Sennacherib had returned home to Nineveh and remained there … until he was killed by two of his sons. Our God will not be mocked!

~

19

"SET YOUR AFFAIRS IN ORDER."

~

*T*he entire kingdom was aware King Hezekiah had no heir to the throne. My daughter, Hephzibah, had not yet borne him children during their three years of marriage. Before, everyone's thoughts had been preoccupied with the Assyrian threats; but now, without those to distract us, the lack of an heir was a growing concern.

No one was more anxious than Hezekiah and my daughter. My precious wife and I continued to reassure them God would be faithful to provide an heir in His timing, but He had not given me a specific message of assurance for them. It soon became obvious what a toll worry was taking on them both emotionally and physically.

But I also noticed how quickly Hezekiah tired – much too fast for a man in his late thirties, even one who bore the responsibilities of a king. I suggested he talk to his physicians and see if they had a remedy to help him regain his energy and strength.

Unfortunately, his physicians were little help. They could not find anything wrong with him physically, and none of their remedies worked. I prayed that Jehovah Rapha would strengthen His servant and take away whatever was afflicting his body.

But as the weeks passed, there was no improvement. As a matter of fact, sores began to develop on Hezekiah's body. One night as I cried out to God, the Lord gave me a message for the king. But like many others over the years, it was not a message I looked forward to sharing.

When I arrived at the Great Hall the next morning, Hezekiah was still in his bed chambers. Apparently, he had not felt strong enough to get out of bed. I went to his room and found him surrounded by my daughter and several physicians. They all looked worried, but no one seemed to know what to do.

"My king," I began, *"I have come to you with a message from the Lord. He says, 'Set your affairs in order, for you are going to die. You will not recover from this illness.'"* [1]

I heard the physicians gasp. They started to contradict me but realized they could not challenge the word of the Lord. My daughter looked at me in horror as tears streamed down her cheeks. Hezekiah turned his face away from me toward the wall and prayed out loud.

"Remember, O Lord," he prayed, *"how I have always tried to be faithful to You and do what is pleasing in Your sight."* [2]

Then he broke down and began to weep bitterly.

My daughter cried out, "No, father! That can't be right! Surely Jehovah God will not let my husband die!"

I had wrestled with God over the message throughout the night, saying: "This king has sought to honor You in word and deed with all his heart. He has not retreated from the task You have given him. He has led Your people to honor You and worship you. He has never once turned to the right or the left. In Your mercy, Oh Lord, heal Hezekiah and grant him life … not death."

But I had not sensed any release from the message God had given me. And now my heart was broken as I listened to Hezekiah and my daughter weep. My heart was broken for our people who would soon hear the news about their king. My heart was broken for my own pain. My heart was broken that I had been the one to deliver the message.

Though I knew God understood our pain, I questioned why He would not answer our prayer. Though I knew God in His infinite wisdom knew what was best for us all, I questioned why in His sovereignty He would not make this right. Though I knew God loved Hezekiah even more than I did, I questioned why His answer reflected so little compassion.

Dealing with my own emotions, plus watching this young couple's agony, I suddenly felt like I was drowning in sorrow. I needed to escape for a while and find a place where I could be alone with God.

As I walked outside into the courtyard, the warmth of the morning sun touched my face. It felt as if God were embracing me and giving me comfort. I felt Him draw me close and say: "Go back to Hezekiah and give him this message!"

∾

20

TEN DEGREES BACKWARD

∼

J walked back into Hezekiah's chamber and announced to him and Hephzibah: "This is what the Lord, the God of your ancestor David, says. 'I have heard your prayer and seen your tears. I will heal you, and three days from now you will get out of bed and go to the temple of the Lord. I will add fifteen years to your life.'"[1]

I called to the servants waiting just outside my son-in-law's chamber. "Make an ointment from figs and spread it over the sores on his body."[2]

The physicians again looked at me with disbelief, but just like before they knew better than to contradict the prophet of the Lord. Hezekiah cautiously asked, "What sign will the Lord give to prove that He will heal me and that I will go to the temple of the Lord three days from now?"[3]

"Throughout your days," I told him, "you have seen the faithfulness of the Lord your God. He has delivered you from the hands of your enemies. He has prospered you and granted you His favor in all your dealings. Whatever He has promised, He has accomplished. He does not lie. But now you ask for a sign from Him?"

. . .

"Your words that I am to set my affairs in order still echo in my ears," Hezekiah replied. "And now you tell me God has granted me fifteen additional years. How am I to know which statement is the one true message from the Lord our God?"

"This is the sign that the Lord will give you to prove He will do as He promised," I answered. *"Would you like the sundial* in the courtyard of the temple *to go forward ten steps or backward ten steps?"*[4]

He said, *"The shadow always moves forward. Make it go backward instead."*[5]

"I will ask God to do as you have requested," I replied.

And so, the Lord did. The shadow moved backward ten degrees that afternoon and then resumed its forward motion adding forty minutes to that day. God who created all things – including time – altered its natural course that one day to make it a 24-hour and 40-minute day to give Hezekiah a sign!

Each day afterward, Hezekiah regained more strength. By the end of three days, his skin was clear and his sores were gone. On the third day, he got out of bed and entered the temple of the Lord – just as God had promised!

"Lord, You have restored my health and have allowed me to live!" Hezekiah prayed. *"You have rescued me from death and have forgiven all my sins. You have healed me. I will sing Your praises with instruments every day of my life in Your temple."*[6]

News of what God had done for Hezekiah spread throughout the lands. Judah's people rejoiced and praised God. Gifts began to pour into Jerusalem from kings of other nations, expressing their thanks to God for His compassionate mercy to Hezekiah.

. . .

The kings also sent valuable presents as expressions of their high esteem for my son-in-law. His wealth grew, as did his treasury. But there was still one thing he lacked. Nebiah and I knew all too well the cry of his and my daughter's hearts.

Not long after Hezekiah had been healed, God answered that prayer as well.

As he shared with me that Hephzibah was pregnant, Hezekiah told me it was a gift that was even more precious to him than his own life.

When the time was completed, all of Judah celebrated the birth of a son – an heir to the throne! The festivities were even more grand than the party marking Hezekiah's recovery. The people rejoiced that their beloved King Hezekiah now had a son who would reign after him. A son who would continue to lead the people to honor Jehovah God.

Nebiah and I were grandparents! Our hearts were overflowing! I was going to have the opportunity to nurture my grandson just as I had nurtured Hezekiah when he was a boy. It was hard to believe that less than a year earlier, we were mourning our son-in-law's imminent death; but today, we were joining him and our daughter in thanksgiving for a new life.

Hezekiah and Hephzibah named their son Manasseh in honor of Hezekiah's younger brother, whose life had tragically been taken by Ahaz. The name means "God has made me forget all the troubles of my father's house." It was a most fitting name for Hezekiah to give to his son.

Everyone was so joyful ... but little did we know what the birth of this son would mean for us all in the days ahead.

～

21

A KING'S PRIDE

~

$\mathcal{T}$he Lord occasionally called on me to leave Jerusalem and travel into different parts of the wilderness east of the city. It was often during those times of prayer and fasting that He gave me messages for His people. After extending Hezekiah's life, the Lord seemed to be leading me out into the wilderness more often.

Throughout that time, the Lord God Jehovah continued to bless the reign of Hezekiah. The king had to build additional treasury buildings to hold the accumulation of silver, gold, precious stones, and spices, as well as for the shields and other items of value.

He also constructed more storehouses for the plentiful harvests of grain and the new wine and olive oil they produced. Many new stalls were built to accommodate the great increase in his herds and flocks. By the will and grace of God, he succeeded in everything he did.

But throughout my times in the wilderness, the Lord continued to remind me that Judah would one day be conquered just as the northern kingdom of Israel had been. Our people would be taken into captivity and scattered like the people of Israel. The threat might come from Assyria, or it could come from another quarter – the growing kingdom of Babylon.

The Lord showed me that kingdoms come, and kingdoms go – only the Lord God Jehovah remains. He permits kings and kingdoms to rise and fall – and through them His will is accomplished. Though the people of Judah may be scattered in captivity and Jerusalem destroyed, the Lord will protect a remnant – one He will use to rebuild His city.

As I was returning to Jerusalem from one of those times in the wilderness, what looked like a royal delegation passed me on the road. Evidently, they had come from Jerusalem and were now traveling toward Jericho. They seemed to be in a hurry, as if they were taking news back to the one who had sent them.

I didn't know for certain, but their flamboyant attire and manner made me think they were Babylonians. I decided to go to the Great Hall to see Hezekiah before stopping to see Nebiah. Upon my arrival I asked him, "My king, *what did those men want? Where were they from?*"[1]

"They were envoys from King Baladan of Babylon," he replied. "They arrived unexpectedly and brought gifts from their king. Baladan had heard of my sickness and recovery, and he sent them to express his best wishes."

Hezekiah was so in awe that the Babylonian king would honor him in such a way, he became prideful. He forgot the source of all his blessings and chose to impress the Babylonian king by showing the envoys the great wealth of Judah. He flaunted everything in the treasury buildings, the storehouses, and the armory.

There was nothing in his palace or the kingdom that he did not reveal. His pride blinded him to the reality that his boasts were exposing the kingdom to great threat from the most powerful empire in the region.

. . .

My heart was quickly burdened for what he had done. "My king," I said, *"listen to this message from the Lord Almighty: 'The time is coming when every-thing you have – all the treasures stored up by your ancestors – will be carried off to Babylon. Nothing will be left!*[2] *Some of your own descendants will be taken away into exile. They will become eunuchs who will serve in the palace of Baby-lon's king.'"*[3]

Hezekiah's response took me by surprise: *"This message you have given me from the Lord is good."*[4]

Hezekiah had heard me say his descendants would be taken away. So, he surmised the captivity would not occur during his reign – rather, there would be peace and security for the remainder of his lifetime. Our king had become more concerned about his personal fate than the fate of his people.

It was the first time I had ever been ashamed of this one who had sat at my knee and earnestly taken in the truth and promises of the Lord. Until now, I had seen him seek the Lord on behalf of his people and seek their welfare above his own. But today, I had seen a different Hezekiah – and my heart was broken.

In the months that followed, I repeatedly thought back to the day the Lord had extended Hezekiah's life. I remembered how he had prayed for God's mercy, and how I had interceded on his behalf. I began to wonder if those prayers God granted had taken us down a road that wasn't God's best for His people.

What if God's best had been for Hezekiah to die at that time? But if he had died, who would now be king? Manasseh had not yet been conceived in my daughter's womb. And yet, what kind of king would he be? I was seeing more of Ahaz in the boy than I was seeing Hezekiah – at least the Hezekiah I had known up until now.

I cried out to God for mercy – but I knew difficult days were ahead.

22

A KING IS HONORED

~

Though the Lord showed me defeat, destruction, and captivity lay ahead in our immediate future, He also assured me His deliverance would one day follow. I heard a voice call out, "Shout!"

"What should I shout?"[1] I asked.

An angel said, *"Shout that people are like the grass that dies away. Their beauty fades as quickly as the beauty of flowers in a field. The grass withers and the flowers fade, but the word of our God stands forever.*[2]

"Make a highway for the Lord through the wilderness. Make a straight, smooth road through the desert for our God. Fill the valleys and level the hills. Straighten the curves and smooth the rough spots. For the glory of the Lord will be revealed, and all the people will see it!"[3]

It was the middle of the night. I couldn't sleep, so I left Nebiah in bed and went into another room to pray. That was when I heard the message from the Lord as I was praising Him for His endless goodness, comfort, and assurance. Suddenly, there was a loud knock on the main door of our chambers.

It was Hephzibah! "Father, my husband is asking for you. You must come quickly!"

I followed Nebiah and my daughter into Hezekiah's bed chamber. The king was surrounded by his physicians and several of his officials. Out of the corner of my eye, I saw Manasseh watching from a corner of the room. The king was barely able to speak above a whisper, and even that was with great effort.

"Come closer, Isaiah," he said. "There are but a few grains of sand remaining in the hourglass of my life, and I have something important to say to you. God has been faithful to grant me every day of the fifteen additional years He promised, and I desire to use this last day wisely.

"Since the days of my youth, you have been my teacher, my conscience, and my wise counselor. If I have done any good in my reign as king, it was because you have been right there beside me pointing me in the right direction. And where I have done wrong, it has been because I failed to heed your counsel.

"In a matter of moments, I will take my last breath and your grandson will become your king. He has not sought you out like I did at his age. He has been content to watch from a distance. But I need you to promise me that you will seek him out. He may not know to seek your wise counsel and the messages you carry from the Lord, but you must make sure he hears from you, nonetheless."

"I have promised God I will do so," I replied, "and now I promise you as well, my king. Rest peacefully in the presence of the God you have faithfully followed and obeyed."

. . .

When I turned to go comfort Manasseh, he had gone. He wasn't there to hear his mother cry out when Hezekiah took his last breath. Two of Hezekiah's officials immediately left to go find our new king and tell him his father had died.

All of Judah mourned and honored their beloved king. I, together with his other officials, had assisted Hezekiah in preplanning his own funeral arrangements. He had wanted to lead his people in death just as he had done in life. He had not wanted the responsibility to fall upon Hephzibah or his twelve-year-old son.

Hezekiah's body was buried in the upper area of the royal cemetery near those of King David and King Solomon. It was the section of the cemetery reserved for the great kings of Judah. There was no question among the people that Hezekiah had earned the right to be buried in that place of honor.

To his credit, Manasseh stood beside his mother and presided over his father's funeral arrangements with a strength and maturity that surpassed his years. He declared the thirty days immediately following his father's death to be a time of mourning throughout the land. He sat in the presence of his father's counselors and heeded our advice.

We counseled Manasseh to continue in the ways of his father. We encouraged him to allow the people to complete their days of mourning before enacting any changes. The time would allow them to grieve their former king and begin to embrace their new king.

Numerous people questioned Manasseh's ability to rule wisely because of his age, but those of us who counseled his father would do the same for him. Throughout the days of mourning, he heeded our advice without exception. The days were peaceful and calm.

But the Lord quickened my heart. A storm was coming, and it would come swiftly. The day after the month of mourning concluded ... the storm arrived!

23

A NEW KING, A NEW DAY

~

J was eighty-eight years old when my twelve-year-old grandson became my king. I never expected to live longer than the three kings I had served before him. By His grace, God has given me the health and strength to serve Him faithfully, even now in my old age.

I have seen kings at their best – and at their worst. I have seen people follow their kings at their best – and at their worst. I have seen our kings and our people love God with their whole hearts – and I have seen them turn away from Him. I have seen our kingdom enjoy the great blessings of God – and I have seen us experience His wrath.

I have seen God single-handedly defeat our enemies, and I have seen Him permit them to overrun and defeat us. I have seen the temple and the surrounding hills cleansed so that we might worship God as He has chosen, and I have seen them desecrated by pagan idols and graven images. I have seen the nation exalted in righteousness, and I have seen it destroyed in wickedness.

• • •

And yet, it always amazes me how easily our hearts can be turned away from God. We can so easily forget His blessings from the past and His promises for the future. We can so easily be deceived into thinking our ways are better than His ways and our thoughts are better than His thoughts. Sadly, such was the case with my grandson.

The day after the mourning period for Hezekiah concluded, Manasseh called all the officials and counselors to appear before him in the Great Hall. He thanked us for our service to his father and for our service to him throughout the days of mourning. But then he told us he no longer required our service.

"Many of you men are now well advanced in years," he announced. "And all of you are very tired. It is time for you to enjoy a well-deserved rest. You have long served your king and the kingdom, and now it is time for you to allow others to do the same."

"My king," I replied, "perhaps it would be wise to allow us to assist your new officials as they assume their roles, so they might benefit from the wisdom we have gleaned through the years and be better able to counsel you well."

"Thank you, grandfather," he answered sarcastically, "for always thinking of my best interest, but those I have selected to serve in my court already have my utmost trust and respect. They have already demonstrated a wisdom and understanding that aligns with my thinking. They truly do not require any assistance from you!"

"Your majesty," I continued, "might we inquire as to who these new counselors are?"

"You most definitely may inquire," he answered. "As a matter of fact, they are entering the hall even as we speak."

• • •

We all turned to watch as they approached – there were only a few men I recognized. Many of them were not much older than our king, and those I recognized I knew to be ne'er-do-wells. I feared there wasn't one herald of wise counsel among them.

My daughter had watched silently as her son made his pronouncement, but now seeing how events were unfolding, she spoke up. "Your majesty, perhaps your grandfather's counsel is worthy to reconsider. These young men with their obvious strength and energy could benefit from some time with those who have gone before them."

Manasseh was visibly annoyed. "Thank you, mother. But I must ask that you leave the decisions on ruling our nation to me, the one who has been ordained by your God to do so. It is a new day in Judah. We will not be restricted by the old ways. We must become more like our neighbors, the Assyrians and the Babylonians, if we are going to prosper in the days ahead. We need new thinking, and these men will provide it to me.

"And in the future, Mother, I would ask that you refrain from attempting to counsel me in my Great Hall. As a matter of fact, I would ask that you and those who are no longer serving as my officials leave the hall so I can meet with my new counselors!"

All of us looked at one another, not quite sure what we should do.

Seeing our hesitation, the king continued. "But if you are unable to find your way out of the hall, I can always have my guards show you the way!"

With that, we all turned and walked out. I prayed God would show us what He would have us do next.

24

THE ONE WHOSE COMING IS PROMISED

~

J tossed and turned in bed that night as I worried about what was about to happen in Judah. My spirit was in turmoil, and nothing could put my mind at ease. All of a sudden, I heard familiar voices. I strained to hear what they were saying but couldn't quite make out the words.

I carefully rose out of bed so as not to wake Nebiah and went to the door of our bed chamber. The voices seemed to be coming from the other room.

As I stepped through the door, I was surprised to find myself in a large, open space – and not the room outside our bed chamber! I was immediately washed in a light as bright as the noonday sun. It took a few minutes for my eyes to adjust, but I continued to listen to the voices.

As everything came into focus, I realized I had been here before. This was the place I had heard Jehovah God ask, *"Who will go for Us?"*[1] But this time there wasn't a multitude of people standing around Him. I saw the shapes of only two people off in the distance. Though I could not see their faces, their voices were as clear as if I were standing right beside them.

. . .

All at once, I saw movement as if they were turning to look at me – but I still could not distinguish their features. However, I could tell One of them was speaking to me. His was the voice I recognized. He was the One who had told me to go and tell His people. I listened carefully so I would hear His every word: "You are the messenger I have sent to My people. How have My people responded to My message?"

I answered, "*My work all seems so useless!* There are some who have turned to You and followed You, but there are still others who seem intent on turning away from You. King Hezekiah was intent on obeying You and following You. But now his son, Manasseh, is even more intent on disobeying You and leading Your people to abandon You. *I have spent my strength for nothing and to no purpose at all.*"[(2)]

Jehovah God immediately corrected me. "*Forget all that – it is nothing compared to what I am going to do. For I am about to do a brand-new thing. I will make a pathway through the wilderness for My people to come home. Yes, I will make springs in the desert, so that My people can be refreshed. I have made them for Myself, and they will someday honor Me before the whole world.*"[(3)]

Next, the other One – the One I knew was the Messiah – spoke up, saying, "*He who formed Me in My mother's womb to be His servant, who commissioned Me to bring His people back to Him, has honored Me and given Me strength.*"[(4)]

Jehovah God continued, "*You will do more than restore the people of Israel back to Me. I will make You a Light to the Gentiles, and You will bring My salvation to the ends of the earth.*[(5)]

"*I am the Lord, the Redeemer and Holy One of Israel, and I say to the One who will be despised and rejected by a nation, to the One who is a Servant of rulers: Kings will stand at attention when You pass by. Princes will bow low because the Lord has chosen You. I, the faithful Lord, the Holy One of Israel, choose You.*[(6)]

. . .

"Isaiah, record these words: 'My Servant will prosper; He will be highly exalted. Many will be amazed when they see Him – beaten and bloodied, so disfigured one would scarcely know He was a Person. And when He returns, He will again startle many nations. Kings will stand speechless in His presence. For they will see what they have previously refused to see, and they will understand what they would not hear.'" (7)

I was standing not only in the presence of the Holy One of Israel, but I was also standing before the One who will bring salvation to all the earth. I fell prostrate before them and cried out: "Holy, holy, holy!"

∼

25

A MESSAGE OF SALVATION

~

*A*fter a while, I asked: "Lord, *who will believe Your message? To whom will You reveal Your saving power?*"[1]

He answered, "My Servant will grow up in their presence like a tender green shoot, sprouting from a root in a dry and sterile ground. There will be nothing beautiful or majestic about His appearance, nothing to attract them to Him. He will be despised and rejected – a Man of sorrows, acquainted with the bitterest grief. They will turn their backs on Him and look the other way as He passes by.[2]

"Yet it will be their weaknesses He carries; it will be their sorrows that weigh Him down. They will think His troubles are a punishment from Me for His own sins! But, rather, He will be wounded and crushed for their sins. He will be beaten that they might have peace. He will be whipped so they may be healed.[3]

"All of them have strayed away like sheep. They have left My path to follow their own, just like your King Manasseh. Yet, on the One I send will I lay the guilt and sins of them all![4]

. . .

"My Son whom I send will be oppressed and treated harshly; yet, He will not say a word. He will be led as a Lamb to the slaughter. And as a sheep is silent before the shearers, He will not open His mouth. From prison and trial, they will lead Him away to His death.⁽⁵⁾

"But who among the people will realize that He is dying for their sins – He is suffering their punishment? He will have done no wrong and never will have deceived anyone. He will be buried like a criminal and placed in a rich man's grave. But it will all have been My good plan to crush Him and fill Him with grief.⁽⁶⁾

"And because of what He has experienced, My Righteous Servant will make it possible for many to be counted righteous, for He will bear all their sins. I will give Him the honors of One who is mighty and great, because He exposed Himself to death and bore the sins of many!⁽⁷⁾

"Now, return to the people and tell them, 'Fear not, Jerusalem; you will not live in shame for much longer. Enlarge your house and build an addition. For you will soon be bursting at the seams. Your descendants will include other nations and their cities. The shame of your youth and the sorrows of your disobedience that led to your widowhood will be remembered no more.'⁽⁸⁾

"Tell them, 'The Holy One whom I send will come as the Bridegroom and He will restore you back to Me. Though you abandoned Me, turn to Him and I will take you back. Your sins will be forgiven and forgotten, and you will be clothed in His righteousness.' I, the Lord, have spoken."

Immediately, the place was filled with a great multitude of people, lifting their voices in a chorus, "Holy, holy, holy is the Lord Almighty!" The foundations began to shake as they sang.

The next thing I knew, the shaking had stopped and everything was quiet. I opened my eyes to discover I was lying in my bed. The morning sun was beginning to rise. Nebiah was standing beside our bed looking down at me.

"Husband, Jehovah God has given you another message for His people, hasn't He?"

"Yes, He has!" I replied. "And it is the greatest message He could possibly give. It is a message of the salvation that will come. Manasseh may lead our people to turn away from God once again, as some of our fathers have done before him, but that will not change the fact that a new day is coming.

"The Lord Almighty will spread a wonderful feast in Jerusalem for everyone around the world. It will be a delicious feast. In that day, He will remove the cloud of gloom, the shadow of death that hangs over the earth. He will swallow up death forever! The Sovereign Lord will wipe away all tears.[9]

"He will remove forever all insults and mockery against His land and people. In that day, the people will proclaim, 'This is our God. We trusted in Him, and He saved us. Let us rejoice in the salvation He brings! For the Lord's good hand rests upon us!'[10]

"Nebiah, Jehovah God has given me a message for all generations. It is a message of hope. It is a message of salvation. It is a message about the One who is to come. I pray our people will not turn away from our God – but we have His assurance that even if they do, we will one day rejoice in the blessings that only His salvation can bring! And I can't possibly think of any better news!"

~

26

THE PAGAN SHRINES AND ALTARS RETURN

~

*J*wept as I watched Manasseh undo all his father had accomplished. I could only imagine the sorrow his actions were bringing to Jehovah God. Within the first year of his reign, my grandson had rebuilt all the pagan shrines his father had destroyed.

Each time I attempted to deliver a message from the Lord, I encountered the ridicule of his officials and the rebuff of the king. Manasseh's heart was not only closed to what I had to say, but he would fly into a rage against me – and against Jehovah God. After the last occasion, he ordered that I never again be permitted entry into the Great Hall.

It took no time before the streets and hills, as well as the temple, were dotted with pagan priests, mediums, and psychics. The priests of the Lord were ordered to leave the temple. Asherah poles were again raised, and images of Baal appeared throughout the landscape. A cloud of evil blanketed Jerusalem!

Manasseh's officials wasted no time in finding him a suitable wife. Meshullemeth was the daughter of a sorcerer named Harez, who had been able to keep his witchcraft hidden from Hezekiah. She was a few years older than the king and in her prime childbearing years. The king's counselors wanted their young monarch to father an heir as soon as possible. Meshullemeth could also help school the king and his future heir in the darker pagan arts she had learned from her father.

Hephzibah's attempts to discourage her son from marrying Meshullemeth were rejected, and she, too, was soon cut off from having any contact with him. Evil permeated the palace and had taken control of the king's thoughts and actions.

Meshullemeth gave birth during the first year of Manasseh's reign. Confident he would soon have an heir, the king ordered a great celebration take place throughout the kingdom. However, when the baby turned out to be a girl – a daughter they named Naamah – he demanded the celebration cease. He was so furious the child was not a son, he would have absolutely nothing to do with her.

A plague swept through our land the following year. The Lord did not give me any indication He had sent it as a reprimand for His people. I knew His punishment was still to come. But even if He had not sent the plague, I knew He had permitted it because of the evil that had overtaken His people.

No one was immune from the effects of the plague. One evening I discovered Nebiah lying on the floor of our quarters in the palace. She was delirious, her pallor was yellow, and her body was racked with relentless cold shivers.

The palace physicians were overwhelmed with sick patients and offered little consolation or assistance. The fever did not discriminate. It afflicted those in the fields, as well as those in the palace. It attacked both the old and the young. I soon learned that Manasseh's daughter, Naamah, had also taken sick.

. . .

Within a matter of days, my precious Nebiah and little Naamah both died. Though I had been permitted little contact with my great-granddaughter, I was overcome with grief over both deaths.

The pagan priests began to offer sacrifices night and day to beg Baal to take away the fever. But, to no surprise, their efforts yielded no results. As the death toll began to rise, Manasseh's officials counseled him to offer human sacrifices to satisfy Baal and stop the fever. Instead, he did something that was contrary to his nature. He sent word for me to come to the Great Hall. The Lord told me to come out of mourning and go.

When I arrived, the king said, "Isaiah, the priests of Baal have offered sacrifices to him and pleaded with him to take away the plague, but he has proven himself to either be unwilling or unable to do so. My officials have counseled me to sacrifice children to the gods in order to quench their thirst for blood. But I have decided to try something else instead.

"If your God Jehovah, the God of my father, is truly who you say He is, He can take away the plague. Ask your God to do so, and if He does, I will worship Him."

Though I had learned to be cautious of my grandson's promises, I was still somewhat encouraged by this statement. "King Manasseh," I replied, "by your word I will do as you have asked. But when Jehovah God turns away the plague, do not fail to heed the promise you have made!"

I walked out of the Great Hall and out of the palace into the city. I continued through the city gate, across the valley, and to the hill overlooking the city. When I had climbed high enough to see the entire city, I lifted my arms and cried out to God.

"Lord, prove today You are the God of Israel. Remove this plague from the city and show Your people and this king that You alone are the One who is worthy to be worshiped. Just as You have done for Your people many times before, show them Your majesty."

• • •

By the next morning, everyone who had been sick no longer had a fever. Jehovah God had healed our people and removed the plague. I immediately made my way to the entry doors of the Great Hall.

27

THE EVIL INCREASES

~

*a*s I attempted to enter the Great Hall, my grandson sent word to me through his guards: "Go away, Isaiah, and do not return to my chambers. Our god Baal has removed the plague. Do not bother me about your God anymore!"

I knew the king could not truly believe this, but for whatever reason he had hardened his heart, like the pharaoh of Egypt, and refused to worship the Lord our God.

Ever since Nebiah died, I tended to stay out in the hills for longer periods of time. There was no one waiting for me to return home anymore. Our sons had long ago moved away to other parts of the kingdom, and our daughter, Queen Hephzibah, had died of a broken heart soon after the death of her mother. In many respects, the queen had become a prisoner in her own palace – unloved by her son and deeply wounded by his actions.

As the days passed, Manasseh fell further and further into the pit of darkness. His practice of fortune-telling was well-known throughout the city. Some said he could inspect the livers of sheep sacrificed on pagan altars and know the will of the gods.

Entrails of sacrificed sheep were brought to the Great Hall by the cartload for the king to examine. He had become consumed by the practice, and the smell of rotting animal flesh permeated the palace. It gave me a hint of how repulsive this behavior must be in the nostrils of Jehovah God.

At the same time, Queen Meshullemeth was teaching him the practice of witchcraft. Through fortune-telling he was attempting to see into the future, and now through witchcraft he was attempting to cast spells against his enemies. Over time, his perception of who his enemies were became more distorted. I was certain I was on that list.

Meshullemeth gave birth to another baby daughter during the third year of Manasseh's reign. This time the king was so enraged, he immediately had the baby thrown into the fires in the valley of the son of Hinnom as a sacrifice to Baal.

I would never have believed any king of Judah could be more evil than King Ahaz. But now I was witnessing his grandson – and mine – doing more wickedness than I ever could have imagined. And I knew the Lord's anger was being roused.

Then Manasseh had a carved idol made and placed in the temple of the Lord. He set it in the very place God had told Solomon: "*I have chosen this place for making sacrifices to Me. I will listen to every prayer made in this place, for I have chosen this temple and set it apart to be My home forever.*"[1]

The Lord said to me, "*Tell Manasseh that thus says the Lord: 'Your hands are the hands of murderers, and your fingers are filthy with sin. Your mouth is full of lies, and your lips are tainted with corruption.*[2]

"You spend your time and energy spinning evil plans that end up in deadly actions. All your activity is filled with sin. Violence is your trademark. Your feet run to do evil, and you rush to commit murder. Wherever you go, misery and destruction follow you.

"That is why I will not punish those who injure you. For your sins are piled up before Me and testify against you. Your sins have cut you off from Me. Because of your sin, I have turned away and will not listen anymore.

"Weep, you people of Judah! Shave your heads in sorrow, for the children you love will be snatched away, and you will never see them again. They will be exiled to distant lands."

I passed by the temple as I returned to the city. Manasseh was outside presenting a sacrifice on his blasphemous altar to his pagan god. He could hide from me behind the doors of the Great Hall, but now he was standing right before me. The Lord told me: "This is the time to confront him with My message!"

Without hesitation, I called out, "King Manasseh, thus says the Lord of hosts." I then told him what the Lord had said, concluding with "... they will be exiled to distant lands."

When I finished, Manasseh called out to his guards. "Arrest this false prophet and take him in shackles to the Great Hall to stand in judgment before me!"

∾

28

"THERE WILL BE NO PEACE FOR THE WICKED."

～

I had been in this Great Hall many times throughout my life. I had stood beside my childhood friend and cousin Jotham, listening with interest to the commands and rulings of his father, King Uzziah. I again stood beside that same friend as his chief counselor when he was king.

I had stood in the presence of King Ahaz before he banished me from the palace. I had returned to serve my student, son-in-law, and king – Hezekiah – counseling him with the words of the Lord. But I had never stood in this Great Hall shackled in chains as a prisoner to be judged by the king. Even Ahaz, for all his wickedness, had known better than to judge God's prophet.

Manasseh sat before me on his elevated throne. His officials sat in two rows extending the length of the hall on either side of me. Guards stood behind me with weapons pointed in my direction.

My grandson was permitting his officials to mock and ridicule me, and they were enjoying it tremendously.

. . .

"Old man, we have grown tired of your threats and those of your God," one councilor said. "Manasseh is king over our land, and Baal is our god. This is a time for fresh thinking and new words from young men who have vision. This is not a time for us to listen to the old stories about a worn-out God from our past. He has grown feeble, just as you have!

"How dare you speak to our king as you just did in the city square! You are a stiff-necked old man, and your disrespect to our king is treason! You will bow before him and pledge to serve him from this day forward. Furthermore, you will denounce your God and declare to the people that Baal alone is god! Otherwise, by order of this council and your king, you will be put to death!"

The king stood to his feet and stared at me, his eyes filled with hatred. "Isaiah, what say you? Will you denounce your God and worship Baal? And will you now bow before me, turn from the things of the past, and follow me into the future?"

I could feel the Spirit of the Lord giving me the words to answer and the boldness to do so. "Your majesty, *I will tell you new things I have not mentioned before; secrets you have not yet heard. They are brand new, not things from the past. So you cannot say, 'We knew that all the time!'*[1]

"Members of the council, *I will tell you of things that are entirely new, for I know so well what traitors you are! You have been rebels from your earliest childhood, rotten through and through.*[2]

"The Holy One of Israel says, *'For My own sake and for the honor of My name, I will hold back My anger and not wipe you out. I will refine you in the furnace of suffering. I will rescue you for My sake – yes, for My own sake. That way the pagan nations will not be able to claim that their gods have conquered Me. I will not let them have My glory!'*[3]

. . .

"Thus says the Sovereign Lord, *'Listen to Me, O family of Jacob, Israel My chosen one! I alone am God, the First and the Last. It was My hand that laid the foundations of the earth. The palm of My right hand spread out the heavens above. I spoke and they came into being.*[(4)]

"He also says, *'I am the Lord your God who teaches you what is good and leads you along the paths you should follow. Oh, that you had listened to My commands! Then you would have had peace flowing like a gentle river and righteousness rolling like waves.*[(5)]

"'*You would have become as numerous as the sands along the seashore – too many to count! There would have been no need for your destruction. But instead there will be no peace for the wicked!'*[(6)] Thus says the Lord God Jehovah."

The council members rose to their feet, their faces contorted with anger and loathing. They looked as if they were ready to execute me.

The councilor who had spoken before said, "Your majesty, we will not listen to any more of this! Render your judgment upon him! The executioner is waiting at the door. Do not permit him to wait any longer!"

My grandson looked at me and said, "Isaiah, tomorrow at dawn you will be put to death at the hand of your executioner in the most horrifying manner we can devise. You will wish you had bowed before me this day. But before your executioner is finished – you will cry out to me for mercy!"

I had never seen such hostility and wickedness in a person's eyes as I saw in my grandson's. Evil had completely overtaken him.

"Guards, take him away!" he shouted.

∼

29

"I WILL GIVE BEAUTY FOR ASHES."

~

I had never been in this part of the palace before. To my knowledge, the dungeon had rarely been used during the reigns of Manasseh's predecessors. But it appeared that my grandson used it often. The smell of death filled my nostrils.

The guards' torches illuminated every conceivable instrument of death and torture. We passed cells housing what I assumed were other prisoners. The faint torchlight revealed men either lying lifeless in a heap or burrowed into the corner of their cell. The sounds of death and dismay echoed throughout the prison.

The guards did not speak as they led me to my cell. When we arrived, they pushed me through the small, gated opening and locked it behind me. Darkness blanketed me as their torches faded into the distance.

I quickly realized the cell's five-foot ceiling prevented me from standing up. As my eyes adjusted to the darkness, I noticed it was a very small space. There was nothing to sit or lie down on – just the dirt floor of the cold, damp stone cave. I'm sure neither my grandson, nor anyone else, was concerned about my lack of comfort.

I found a spot where I could sit with my back against the stone wall. It was near the opening so I could breathe a little air. I closed my eyes and spoke to God for the first time since He told me to confront Manasseh.

"Lord, I am Your messenger. The words I spoke were the words You gave me. I pray You have found me faithful to You and to the task You set before me. I do not know everything tomorrow will bring, but I pray You will find me faithful to the very end. Show me clearly what You would have me do – and give me the faith and strength to finish well."

As I sat there in that dingy cell with my eyes closed, I was suddenly transported to the great room in the heavens where Jehovah God had brought me twice before. This time, there was only One standing before me. He looked at me with compassion as He said, *"The Spirit of the Sovereign Lord is upon Me, because He has appointed Me to bring good news to the poor. He has sent Me to comfort the brokenhearted and to announce that captives will be released, and prisoners will be freed.*[1]

"He has sent Me to tell those who mourn that the time of the Lord's favor has come, and with it, the day of God's anger against their enemies. To all who mourn, He will give beauty for ashes, joy instead of mourning, praise instead of despair. For the Lord has planted them like strong and graceful oaks for His own glory.[2]

"And Isaiah, that is not only true when the Father's time comes to pass for Me to go to earth, it is also true today – and it is true for you! Through Me, He will give you beauty for ashes, joy instead of mourning, and praise instead of despair!

"You have remained faithful to the end, and I will be right there with you as you walk through these final hours. I will not leave you nor forsake you. Though you have been despised, hated, and rebuffed by all, you will be a joy to future generations for I will make you so. The Lord delights in you and will claim you as His own.

. . .

"The day is coming when I will create a new heaven and a new earth – so wonderful no one will even think about the old ones anymore. Be glad; rejoice forever in My creation. And look! I will create Jerusalem as a place of happiness and her people will be a source of joy.

"I will rejoice in Jerusalem and delight in My people. And the sound of weeping and crying will be heard no more. Isaiah, though weeping may endure for a night, joy will come in the morning!"

Just then, I heard the footsteps of the guards approaching, and the light from their torches began to illuminate my cell.

∾

30

"AND HE SHALL REIGN FOREVER AND EVER!"

~

"Stand up, Isaiah!" the guards yelled. "Your appointed hour has come!"

They led me in shackles to the palace courtyard. Apparently, my execution would not take place in the darkness of the dungeon but rather out in the open for others to witness. Even though the sun was just beginning to rise, I could see the hatred etched on the faces of Manasseh's officials as they stood before me. They looked deranged as they shouted with one voice, "Death to the one who speaks falsely against his king!"

A wooden platform had been constructed overnight in the center of the courtyard with twelve rugged steps leading up to it. A large, roughly hewn wooden table had been placed in the center of the platform. Two men, who evidently were my executioners, stood on opposite sides of the table. Three guards led me onto the platform and told me to gaze up at one of the palace windows.

I saw Manasseh looking down at me with disgust and resentment. There was no question the one truly overseeing this moment was the evil one.

Manasseh and the others had simply become pawns in his hands. The evil one feared the One whose coming I had foretold more than anything else, and he sought to silence my voice.

"My king," I shouted up to Manasseh, "it is still not too late for you to seek the Lord God Jehovah and turn from your evil ways. If you turn to Him in repentance, He will forgive you and heal your land. But if you do not, you will soon hear the marching feet of the Assyrian army as they come to take you captive. You will be bound as I am now and led away to a place you do not want to go."

The king's face remained unchanged as he stood there in silence. He simply signaled to the executioners to proceed. The guards removed my shackles, then tied my hands and my feet with ropes. They laid me on the table and bound my chest and legs to it so I could not move.

I saw the instrument to be used in my execution. It was a crosscut saw with handles on both ends. As I looked closer, I realized the saw had not been fashioned from metal but from wood. The executioners took their positions, one on each side of the table.

Apparently, the king had determined sawing my body in half with a dull wooden blade was the horrifying torture he sought. The dullness would prolong the agony.

I knew I would soon be in the presence of the Holy One of Israel. But this time, I would not enter His presence through a vision – this time I would be there in person. As I looked up, the heavens parted, and I saw the One whose coming I had foretold. He looked at me with compassion and assurance.

Surrounding Him was a multitude who formed a great cloud of witnesses. Some of the faces looked familiar, but others did not. However, I knew these men and women had one thing in common. They all looked forward by faith to the coming arrival of the Promised One – the One who promises He will never leave us nor forsake us.

. . .

As my executioners went about their task, I was no longer conscious of what they were doing. Rather, I was acutely aware of the beckoning of my Lord. He was more real to me now than anyone standing around me or anyone I had known on this earth. He stood with arms outstretched, welcoming me home into His kingdom. Everything around me would one day pass away, but His kingdom would endure forever.

And I heard those gathered around Him proclaiming His royal titles: "*Wonderful Counselor, Almighty God, Everlasting Father, Prince of Peace.*[1] Hallelujah! For the Lord God Omnipotent reigns ... and He shall reign forever and ever!"

～

PLEASE HELP ME BY LEAVING A REVIEW!

i would be very grateful if you would leave a review of this book. Your feedback will be helpful to me in my future writing endeavors and will also assist others as they consider picking up a copy of the book.

To leave a review:

Go to: amazon.com/dp/1736715569

Or scan this QR code using your camera on your smartphone:

Thanks for your help!

~

YOU WILL WANT TO READ ALL OF THE BOOKS IN "THE CALLED" SERIES

Stories of these ordinary men and women called by God to be used in extraordinary ways.

A Carpenter Called Joseph (Book 1)

A Prophet Called Isaiah (Book 2)

A Teacher Called Nicodemus (Book 3)

A Judge Called Deborah (Book 4)

A Merchant Called Lydia (Book 5)

A Friend Called Enoch (Book 6)

A Fisherman Called Simon (Book 7)

A Heroine Called Rahab (Book 8)

A Witness Called Mary (Book 9) releasing March 24

A Cupbearer Called Nehemiah (Book 10) releasing June 16

THROUGH THE EYES

... the complete *"THROUGH THE EYES"* SERIES

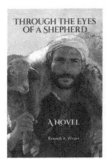  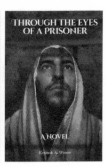

Experience the truths of Scripture as these stories unfold through the lives and eyes of a shepherd, a spy and a prisoner. Rooted in biblical truth, these fictional novels will enable you to draw beside the storytellers as they worship the Baby in the manger, the Son who took up the cross, the Savior who conquered the grave, the Deliverer who parted the sea and the Eternal God who has always had a mission.

Through the Eyes of a Shepherd (Book 1)

Through the Eyes of a Spy (Book 2)

Through the Eyes of a Prisoner (Book 3)

AVAILABLE IN PAPERBACK, LARGE PRINT, AND FOR KINDLE ON AMAZON.

Scan this QR code using your camera on your smartphone to see the entire series on Amazon:

∿

THE EYEWITNESSES COLLECTION

... you will also want to read "The Eyewitnesses" Collection

The first four books in these collections of short stories chronicle the first person eyewitness accounts of eighty-five men, women and children and their unique relationships with Jesus.

Little Did We Know – the advent of Jesus (Book 1)

Not Too Little To Know – the advent – ages 8 thru adult (Book 2)

The One Who Stood Before Us – the ministry and passion of Jesus (Book 3)

The Little Ones Who Came – the ministry and passion – ages 8 thru adult (Book 4)

The Patriarchs — eyewitnesses from the beginning — Adam through Moses tell their stories (Book 5) — releasing in 2023

Now available through Amazon.

Scan this QR code using your camera on your smartphone to see the entire collection on Amazon:

~

LESSONS LEARNED IN THE WILDERNESS SERIES

The Lessons Learned In The Wilderness series

A non-fiction series of devotional studies

There are lessons that can only be learned in the wilderness experiences of our lives. As we see throughout the Bible, God is right there leading us each and every step of the way, if we will follow Him. Wherever we are, whatever we are experiencing, He will use it to enable us to experience His Person, witness His power and join Him in His mission.

The Journey Begins (Exodus) – Book 1

The Wandering Years (Numbers and Deuteronomy) – Book 2

Possessing The Promise (Joshua and Judges) – Book 3

Walking With The Master (The Gospels leading up to Palm Sunday) – Book 4

Taking Up The Cross (The Gospels – the passion through ascension) – Book 5

Until He Returns (The Book of Acts) – Book 6

The complete series is also available in two e-book boxsets or two single soft-cover print volumes.

Now available through Amazon.

Scan this QR code using your camera on your smartphone to see the entire series on Amazon:

—————

For more information, go to:

wildernesslessons.com or kenwinter.org

ALSO AVAILABLE AS AN AUDIOBOOK

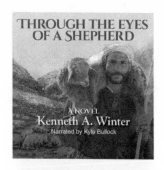

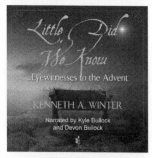

SCRIPTURE BIBLIOGRAPHY

∼

Much of the story line of this book is taken from the books of 2 Kings, 2 Chronicles, and Isaiah. Certain fictional events or depictions of those events have been added.

Some of the dialogue in this story are direct quotations from Scripture. Here are the specific references for those quotations:

Chapter 1

[1] Amos 3:1-2

[2] Amos 3:6-7

[3] Amos 3:8

[4] Amos 2:4-5

Chapter 2

[1] 2 Chronicles 26:18

Chapter 4

[1] Isaiah 6:3

[2] Isaiah 6:3

Chapter 5

[1] Isaiah 6:5

[2] Isaiah 6:7

[3] Isaiah 6:8

[4] Isaiah 6:8

[5] Isaiah 6:9

[6] Isaiah 6:11

[7] Isaiah 6:11-13

Chapter 6

[1] Amos 7:7-9

[2] Amos 9:11-12

Chapter 8

[1] Deuteronomy 2:19

[2] 1 Samuel 11:11

Chapter 9

[1] Isaiah 5:1-6

[2] Isaiah 5:30

Chapter 10

[1] Isaiah 7:4, 7

[2] Isaiah 7:11

[3] Isaiah 7:12

[4] Isaiah 7:14

[5] Isaiah 7:17, 20

[6] Isaiah 7:21, 22, 25

[7] Isaiah 8:11-13, 22

Chapter 11

[1] 2 Chronicles 28:9-11

[2] 2 Chronicles 28:13

[3] 2 Kings 16:7

Chapter 13

[1] Isaiah 8:16; 9:1-2

[2] Isaiah 9:4, 6

[3] Isaiah 9:7

[4] Isaiah 10:4-5

[5] Isaiah 10:6-7

[6] Isaiah 10:12, 18-19

[7] Isaiah 10:20-22

[8] Isaiah 10:24-25, 34

[9] Isaiah 11:1, 6

Chapter 14

[1] 2 Chronicles 29:5-6

[2] 2 Chronicles 29:6, 8

[3] 2 Chronicles 29:10-11

[4] 2 Chronicles 30:6-9 (paraphrase)

Chapter 15

[1] Isaiah 14:29-31 (portions)

Chapter 16

[1] 2 Kings 18:14

[2] 2 Kings 18:14 (paraphrase)

Chapter 17

[1] 2 Chronicles 32:7-8

(2) 2 Kings 18:19-21

(3) 2 Kings 18:22; 2 Chronicles 32:13-14

(4) 2 Chronicles 32:15

(5) 2 Kings 18:23-25

(6) 2 Kings 18:31-32

(7) Isaiah 37:3-4

(8) Isaiah 37:6-7

Chapter 18

(1) Isaiah 37:23-29

(2) Isaiah 37:33-35

Chapter 19

(1) Isaiah 38:1

(2) Isaiah 38:3

Chapter 20

(1) 2 Kings 20:5-6

(2) 2 Kings 20:7

(3) 2 Kings 20:8

(4) 2 Kings 20:9

(5) 2 Kings 20:10

(6) Isaiah 38:16, 17, 20

Chapter 21

(1) Isaiah 39:3

(2) Isaiah 39:5-6

(3) Isaiah 39:7

(4) Isaiah 39:8

Chapter 22

(1) Isaiah 40:6

(2) Isaiah 40:6-7

(3) Isaiah 40:3-5

Chapter 24

(1) Isaiah 6:8

(2) Isaiah 49:4

(3) Isaiah 43:18-21

(4) Isaiah 49:5

(5) Isaiah 49:6

(6) Isaiah 49:7

(7) Isaiah 52:13-15

Chapter 25

(1) Isaiah 53:1

(2) Isaiah 53:2-3

(3) Isaiah 53:4-5

(4) Isaiah 53:6

(5) Isaiah 53:7-8

(6) Isaiah 53:8-10

(7) Isaiah 53:11-12

(8) Isaiah 54:2-4

(9) Isaiah 25:6-8

(10) Isaiah 25:8-10

Chapter 27

(1) 2 Chronicles 7:12, 15-16

(2) Isaiah 59:3

Chapter 28

(1) Isaiah 48:6-7

(2) Isaiah 48:8

(3) Isaiah 48:9-11

(4) Isaiah 48:12-13

(5) Isaiah 48:17-18

(6) Isaiah 48:19, 22

Chapter 29

(1) Isaiah 61:1

(2) Isaiah 61:2-3

Chapter 30

(1) Isaiah 9:6

∼

LISTING OF CHARACTERS
(ALPHABETICAL ORDER)

∿

Many of the characters in this book are real people pulled directly from the pages of Scripture. i have not changed any details about those individuals except in some instances their interactions with the fictional characters. They are noted below as "UN" (unchanged).

In other instances, fictional details have been added to real people to provide additional background about their lives where Scripture is silent. The intent is to provide further information for the story. They are noted as "FB" (fictional background).

In some instances, we are never told the names of certain individuals in the Bible. In those instances, where i have given them a name as well as a fictional background, they are noted as "FN" (fictional name).

Lastly, a few of the characters are purely fictional, added to convey the fictional elements of these stories . They are noted as "FC" (fictional character).

∿

Abijah – wife of Ahaz, daughter of King Zechariah of Israel (FB)
Abraham – the patriarch (UN)

Ahaz – 12th king of Judah, son of Jotham, father of Hezekiah, nephew of Isaiah (FB)

Ahio – wife of Jotham (FN)

Amaziah – 9th king of Judah, son of Joash, father of Uzziah, uncle of Isaiah (UN)

Amos – a prophet of God (FB)

Amoz – son of Joash, brother of Amaziah, father of Isaiah (UN)

Angel of the Lord - worshiping the Lord before His throne (UN)

Azariah – a high priest during King Uzziah's reign (UN)

Azrikam – commander of the palace of Judah under King Ahaz (UN)

David – king of Israel (before the kingdoms divided) (UN)

Elkanah – commander of the army of Judah under King Ahaz (UN)

Hanun – king of Ammon early 10th century BC, son of Nahash (UN)

Hephzibah – daughter of Isaiah and Nebiah, wife of Hezekiah, mother of Manasseh (FB)

Hezekiah – 13th king of Judah, son of Ahaz, father of Manasseh, son-in-law of Isaiah (FB)

Isaiah – a prophet of God, son of Amoz (FB)

Jecoliah – wife of Amaziah (UN)

Jehoaddan – wife of Joash (UN)

Jehoshaphat – 4th king of Judah, son of Asa, father of Jehoram (UN)

Jehovah God – the Sovereign and Almighty God (UN)

Jerushah – wife of Uzziah, mother of Jotham and Nebiah (FB)

Joash – 8th king of Judah, father of Amaziah and Amoz, grandfather of Isaiah (UN)

Jotham – 11th king of Judah, son of Uzziah, father of Ahaz, cousin and brother-in-law of Isaiah (FB)

Lot – nephew of Abraham (UN)

Maher-shalal-hash-baz – second son of Isaiah and Nebiah (FB)

Manasseh – 2nd son of Ahaz, sacrificed to pagan gods as a child (FC)

Manasseh – 14th king of Judah, son of Hezekiah (FB)

Meshullemeth – wife of Manasseh (FN)

Messiah, the Promised One – the Son of the Living God (UN)

Naamah – 1st daughter of Manasseh, great granddaughter of Isaiah (FC)

Nahash – king of Ammon mid 11th century BC (UN)

Nebiah – daughter of Uzziah, wife of Isaiah (FN)

Oded – a prophet of God (UN)

Pekah – 18th king of the northern kingdom of Israel (UN)

Rab-shakeh – Assyrian general under King Sennacherib (UN)

Rezin – king of Aram (UN)

Sennacherib – king of Assyria 705 – 681 BC (UN)

Shanip – king of Ammon mid 8th century BC (UN)

Shear-Jashub – oldest son of Isaiah and Nebiah (FB)

Solomon – king of Israel (before the kingdoms divided) (UN)

Tiglath – 3rd son of Ahaz (named in honor of Tiglath-Pileser), sacrificed to pagan gods as a child (FC)

Tiglath-Pileser III – king of Assyria 745 – 727BC (UN)

Unnamed daughter of Manasseh – 2nd daughter, sacrificed to pagan gods at birth (FC)

Uzziah – 10th king of Judah, son of Amaziah, father of Jotham, cousin of Isaiah (FB)

~

ACKNOWLEDGMENTS

I do not cease to give thanks for you ....
Ephesians 1:16 (ESV)

... my partner in all things, LaVonne,
for choosing to trust God as we follow Him in this faith adventure
together;

... my family,
for your love, support and encouragement;

... Sheryl,
for always helping me tell the story in a better way;

... Scott,
for the way you use your creative abilities to bring glory to God;

... a great group of friends who have read an advance copy of this book,
for all of your help, feedback and encouragement;

... and most importantly,
the One who is truly the Author and Finisher of it all
– our Lord and Savior Jesus Christ!

∾

ABOUT THE AUTHOR

Ken Winter is a follower of Jesus, an extremely blessed husband, and a proud father and grandfather – all by the grace of God. His journey with Jesus has led him to serve on the pastoral staffs of two local churches – one in West Palm Beach, Florida and the other in Richmond, Virginia – and as the vice president of mobilization of the IMB, an international missions organization.

Today, Ken continues in that journey as a full-time author, teacher and speaker. You can read his weekly blog posts at kenwinter.blog and listen to his weekly podcast at kenwinter.org/podcast.

And we proclaim Him, admonishing every man and teaching every man with all wisdom, that we may present every man complete in Christ. And for this purpose also I labor, striving according to His power, which mightily works within me.
(Colossians 1:28-29 NASB)

PLEASE JOIN MY READERS' GROUP

Please join my Readers' Group in order to receive updates and information about future releases, etc.

Also, i will send you a free copy of *The Journey Begins* e-book — the first book in the *Lessons Learned In The Wilderness* series. It is yours to keep or share with a friend or family member that you think might benefit from it.

It's completely free to sign up. i value your privacy and will not spam you. Also, you can unsubscribe at any time.

Go to kenwinter.org to subscribe.

Or scan this QR code using your camera on your smartphone:

∽